Hope you enjoy —

Vannie Abner

HEIR TO THESE HILLS

HEIR TO THESE HILLS

by

Vannie Abner

FIRST EDITION

Printed in the United States of America

Dedicated to my aunt
Louise B. Taylor
and other believers—

All is true.
SHAKESPEARE

ACKNOWLEDGMENTS

The following have generously donated time and energy to this story's makeup, and I wish to thank them:

Nannie Butts
Lester and Berniece Capps
Dr. Ruth Dowling
James Harlan
Fern Moreland
Robbie Morgan
Gloria Nelson
Elma Ratz
G. T. Richards
Barbara Young
and
Estel and Nettie Morgan, whose patience and willingness especially inspired this writer throughout the making of this story.

Photographs are courtesy of Estel and Nettie Morgan, Robbie Morgan, G. T. Richards, and Barbara Young. Additional photography work by Bill Mason.

CONTENTS

Photographs, throughout.

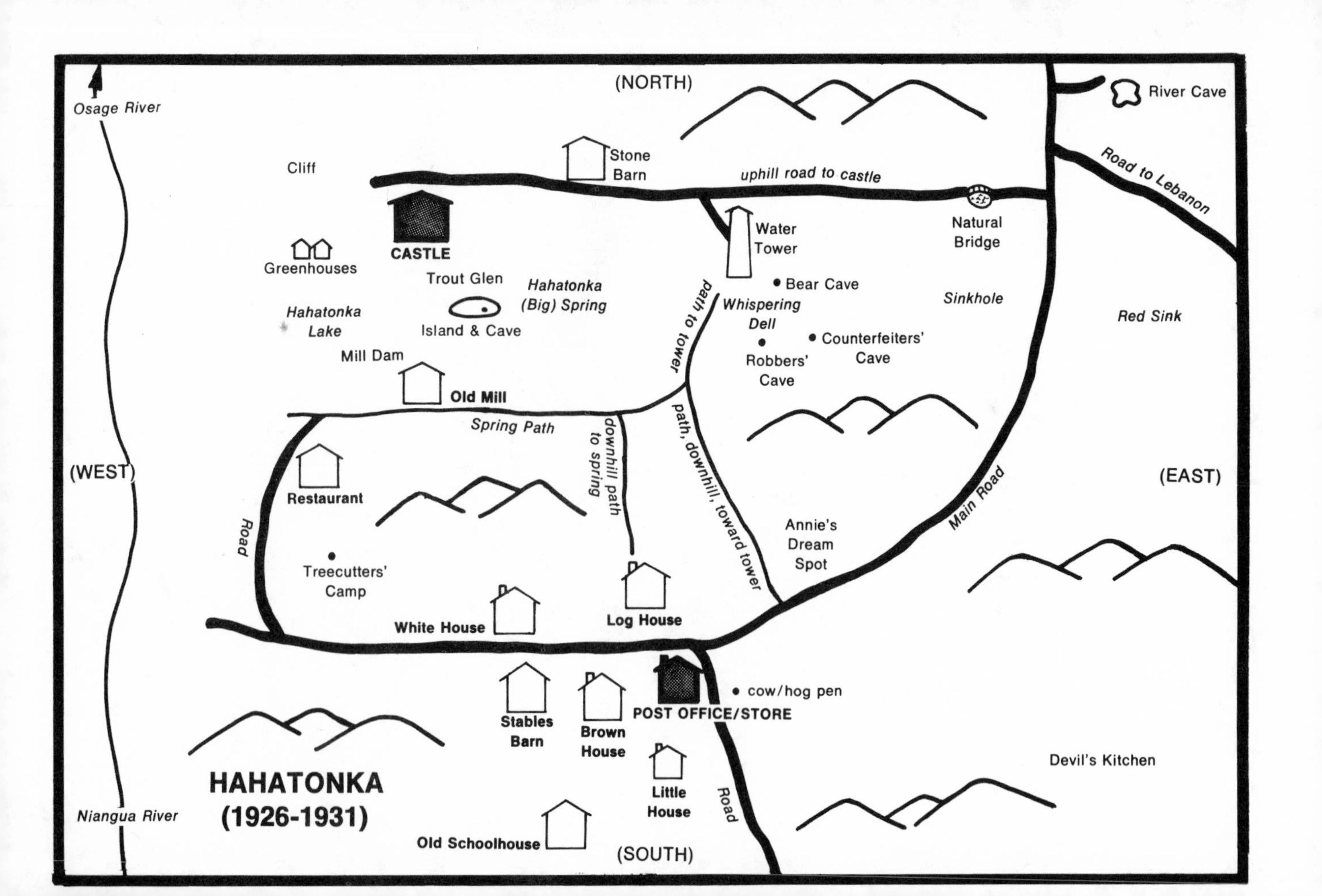

HAHATONKA
(1926-1931)
(NORTH)
(SOUTH)
(EAST)
(WEST)
Osage River
Niangua River
River Cave
Road to Lebanon
Cliff
Stone
Barn
uphill road to castle
Natural
Bridge
CASTLE
Greenhouses
Water
Tower
Trout Glen
Hahatonka
(Big) Spring
Bear Cave
Sinkhole
Red Sink
Hahatonka
Lake
Island & Cave
path to tower
Whispering
Dell
Counterfeiters'
Cave
Robbers'
Cave
Mill Dam
Old Mill
Spring Path
downhill path
to spring
path, downhill, toward tower
Main Road
Restaurant
Road
Annie's
Dream
Spot
Treecutters'
Camp
White House
Log House
cow/hog pen
POST OFFICE/STORE
Stables
Barn
Brown
House
Little
House
Road
Devil's Kitchen
Old Schoolhouse

Chapter I

INTRODUCTION

These hills, that have homed almost every kind of critter nameable (and some that aren't), have their own name—Hahatonka. Their legend is such that one could be easily and rightfully lost in sheer reverie by hearing it; so, to assist you in grasping rhyme and reason of what follows, first I'll provide you with fact, pure and plain, then tell the entire story without the aid of my imagination.

These hills stand in Ozark country, a land lavishly endowed by God's green thumb. Seems that everywhere the Indians settled their headquarters they had certain criteria for the land, and here they met the best of all worlds. I'm talking about the Osage Indians, who held their pow wows along the Osage River, who hunted their food and clothing in these hills. In 1801 Daniel Boone and his son Nathan paddled up the Osage to trap beaver right here, on a lake that I've spent many evenings pondering, but the rulers of these hills took over the beaver skins. The next winter, to fulfill a contract with a Kentucky hat maker, Daniel and Nathan paddled the same route, trapped more beaver, then found a cave to store the furs in.

Surely the Osages were kings of these hills, until 1806 when President Jefferson sent a message to the chiefs telling them their land belonged to white men. The Osages didn't accept that until 1825 when finally they ceded these hills to the government and moved westward, outside the Missouri boundary.

Then came the white men, settlers they were called, some in glory, some in warfare and hostility, still others in mere pursuit of a home. Among those critters was a man named

Garland who posed as a miller, under the alias John Avy, and built a grist mill, about one fourth mile from a cave where he practiced his real trade—counterfeiting. Though suspected by the few honest settlers, Garland was skillfully drawing so many others into his flock that in no time the lawless greatly outnumbered the lawful and the latter didn't interfere. Garland Presses became renowned as the "Bank of Niangua (the small river that meets the Osage and stems a spring under Counterfeiters' Cave)" and was issuing monies distributed as far as the eastern seaboard cities.

While all frontier lands held their shares of outlaws, these forbidding hills supplied bandits with a surer footing than most so that eventually every variety of crime was booming in these hills. Then, as honest folks saw their lives and properties becoming more insecure, they united for mutual protection.

In 1836 they organized and earned the name "Slickers" because of their way of punishing outlaws. When they caught a wrongdoer, they tied him to a tree and beat him with hickory whips and didn't let up until the rascal promised to leave the territory. Their aim was to resist unlawful attacks, to recover stolen property, and to preserve respectability for an eventual county. Naturally an "Anti-Slickers" group was formed by robbers and counterfeiters to intimidate the menacing opposition by rendering a bold front and placing spies within the "Slickers." There were messy confrontations and settlers would no longer trace stolen goods to Avy's operation since too many men had been killed in its vicinity. It was the "Slicker War," all right.

Seems the outlaws flourished, for a while, and even worked their way into politics after 1841 when Kinderhook County (in 1843 changed to Camden County, for political reasons) developed around these hills. There must have been heated scuffles in that courthouse! About that same time, Avy and his men grew nervous about a report that drastic measures were going to be taken against them, so they counter-plotted to murder a judge and several other active lawmen. Attempting to carry through, they killed a young, well known and well liked man. And that roused the Slickers. They finally mustered the upper hand and almost conquered the Bank of Niangua in one sweep. At least, their attack dampened the "Bankers'" cause, and shortly thereafter Avy himself fled the territory. Niangua was raided a second time, then no men and no machines. But pieces of buried evidence were later found on a nearby farm.

The following years, save a few Civil War skirmishes, these hills echoed mostly sounds of hearty, lawabiding, peaceful settlers, working toward civilization. Then in 1872 these hills acquired a post office and an official name, Gunter's Big Spring, lasting only three years; and in 1882 again a post office was established, called Gunter.

Throughout the years, old men of the Osage Nation had returned to visit their Niangua home, and during a visit they explained to an old settler and Crimean War veteran, Captain Lodge, that they'd always called these hills Hahatonka because young Osages often played on the rivers, and spring and lake, and shouted, "Laughing Waters, Laughing Waters!" In turn, Captain Lodge shared that information with a curious gentleman and Civil War veteran, Colonel Scott, who came to these hills with an engineering crew running a railroad survey. Colonel Scott's persistence in seeing these hills obtain their proper name prompted the Post Office Department, on May 3, 1895, to issue these hills their lasting and fitting title, Hahatonka.

Then Colonel Scott gathered some partners and bought fifty-four hundred acres of Hahatonka and made sure each cave had a name, appropriate to its history; and he took to writing about his property, making Hahatonka the topic of extensive magazine articles, as early as 1898. But Hahatonka didn't stay in Colonel Scott and his partners' hands for long because just a few years later a man, of remarkable foresight and riches, set foot in these hills and saw in them a purpose that no one else could have imagined or fulfilled.

It was one crisp autumn day that Mr. Robert M. Snyder left Kansas City to hunt and fish in the Ozarks. His first stop was a hotel in Lebanon, about twenty-five miles away, where knowledgeable folks directed him to these hills. As soon as he reached Hahatonka, Mr. Snyder saw it from the Osages' view, its unequalled beauty and tranquility, and from the outlaws' view, its inaccessibility, and envisioned his hideaway dream house standing right above Hahatonka Lake. Quick to act on behalf of the dream he'd had, in 1904 Mr. Snyder bought thirty-four hundred acres around Hahatonka Lake and Spring and commenced development of Hahatonka Estate, by means of building roads, stocking a stream with trout, and designing an elaborate blueprint for his property. In 1905 construction of his sixty-two room house, and stables, and greenhouses, and ninety foot water tower, was underway. And all that brings us closer to the story I'm about to tell.

Only one year after his dream world had begun materializing, Mr. Snyder took an ill-fated car ride and met his death in Kansas City. At that, all construction ceased. Stonelayers who'd come from Scotland went to other work, likewise did native workers; glass for the greenhouses lay untouched, and the big house stood in its bare frame. For seventeen years Hahatonka Estate suffered the shock of its forefather's death.

Finally in 1923 Hahatonka Estate began recovering, under the charge of Mr. Snyder's sons, and soon became a liveable community. It was then that Hahatonka took on a new and colorful twist and gave us the following story.

Hereafter, though the folks be actual,
their names are not.

Chapter II

1926

In autumn of 1926 my clan and I left farming to pursue another calling and moved to Hahatonka where we became storekeepers. Since whoever managed the general store automatically acquired the post office duties, my wife Annie was soon officially named Hahatonka's post-mistress. And, not only did we operate those two businesses in that building but also we lived there—upstairs—Annie, our three young ones, and I. We were crowded, and we knew it wasn't going to be anything like living on the farm.

We stood on the road, in front of our new home, and gazed at treetops as, one after another, they lowered then disappeared into a sinkhole then rose again to meet the castle grounds. There it was, that castle, the talk of Camden County, and we were going to live a stone's throw from it.

At that moment, I said to Annie, "I feel like I'm in another world, a foreign land."

"Ely, I think we are."

In any direction we turned there was more wonder, but our eyes returned to that amazing castle.

Someone was leaning over a balcony, trying to catch our attention, a hired helper, we assumed, since he looked like a regular hillbilly. We waved back, glad to see a friendly soul; but then he hurried inside the castle. And somehow our minds turned to matters at hand.

The store looked as if it needed some organization and nothing suited Annie more than to get set for business, so we dug right in. In no time, the door flew open and we had a

"There it was, that castle . . ."

customer, the same gawky, overgrown boy that was on the castle's balcony.

"Got any candy bars and pop?"

No sooner than he'd said that, that boy was eating candy bars, as fast as I could count them, four in all, then drank two bottles of soda.

"How much?"

When I said, "Twenty cents in all," I could tell by his expression that he didn't have enough money.

"Could I pay you later?"

Taking a good look at him, I figured I'd be making a mistake but said anyway, "Sure, tomorrow'll be fine."

Smiling from ear to ear, he said, "I live juss over yonder, in ta big house; I wasa wavin' at ya, while go."

"What do you do there, son?"

"I juss live there; my name's Will."

Wondering about that boy, why his clothes didn't fit and why he was barefoot and if he actually could be a member of the castle clan, I introduced myself and returned to work. Then he went outside to chat with our young ones, while I kept an eye on him and noticed how the children took to him.

Seems our first customer felt at home in the store because he was still there by sunset after giving us his able help in moving and stocking goods. He wouldn't take any pay and wouldn't let us erase his bill and wouldn't stay for supper. And, to my surprise, it wasn't long, yet not the next day, that Will paid his debt—but just in time to rack up another. Amazing how a body could eat so many candy bars and drink so much soda. Though I wondered about him, I soon began liking that boy Will.

Within a couple weeks we were full pledged merchants but with little business. Hahatonka was scarcely populated and not all its citizens shopped in our store. Directly across the road from us, in a big log house, lived a clan who never stepped foot inside the store, at least, to buy goods. If it hadn't been for the post office's location (and several isolated incidents), those folks wouldn't have crossed the road; and, if I hadn't realized early that they were purely city folks, I would have thought it was us that kept them from trading in Hahatonka. As it was, the general store carried only necessities, and at that, only country folks' necessities.

It was us, though, that caused that clan, especially the Mrs., some disturbance in the mornings. Seems they were accustomed to sleeping late because of almost nightly parties while we rose early because of daily duties. And two very different lifestyles, occurring one hundred feet from each other, clashed right off the bat.

We had just bought chickens, fifteen brown Leghorn crowers, that answered day's first ray of light. Upon their third day's announcement, we were visited by the log house's family head.

"My wife requests that your chickens either be quiet until 10:00 a.m. or be done away with. For two mornings she's raised her blindfold to that awful noise, and this a.m. it was more than she could bear. Now she's suffering a tremendous headache."

I was in a pickle, thinking that surely even those city folks knew chickens had to crow at dawn; but I answered as a good neighbor would, "I'll do what I can," having no idea how to keep chickens quiet.

The following morning we awoke to gunfire, fifteen shots behind the store. Funny that we hadn't even noticed the chickens' crowing; guess we were used to the sound, but our neighbors surely weren't. They helped us realize, soon enough, that life in Hahatonka wasn't going to be a bed of roses.

Chapter III

1927

Though our initial adjustment was past, we had only begun meeting surprises and predicaments in our new home as 1927 rolled around. Howling winds surrounded these hills until I thought the trees would blow away. Finally spring came and left like the winter winds, and in no time school was over and all those city folks returned to Hahatonka to spend the summer.

I could see Will coming up the road, walking that peculiar walk of his, almost gorilla-like, swinging his arms as if they were shoving air behind him to propell his body forward. He was a sight for sore eyes and surely was in a hurry to reach the store.

"Look here, Ely, look at what I found down yonder in Devil's Kitchen. A Indian artifact, looks like ta heada a tomahawk! What da ya think?"

Sure enough, Will was holding a piece of equipment that the Osages had left behind, and he was as proud as a cat with a mouse in his paws.

"Ely, I'm goin' keep this and look for more artifacts. I knowed there'd have ta be traces of Indians who lived in these parts. I wanta be a historian when I'm growed up, and any piece of history I find now I can save till I know what ta do with it. Them candy bars and pop sure are temptin'; glad my credit's good here."

My young ones were observing Will's every movement, and he was downright entertaining and even charming, in a very different way. But I doubted his ability to take on such a strenuous study as history.

"Will, how did you fare with school work?"

"Well, Ely," he began, in his slow, sluggish voice, "I got perfect marks 'cept in English. There I gota D. My ma and pa they're used ta it; they hired a tutor when I was juss eight, and that old lady said I lacked d'sire ta grasp holda our language—whatere' that means. My uncle Joe, he lives right there (Sure enough, Will was pointing to the log house.), he tells me ta bad mark this year is 'cause I talk ta hillbillies so much and that I mightn't be able ta talk right 'gain. But I don't understand halfa what he says ta me, must be our minds in different places. Most ever time I see him he asks me why I ain't at home, and I always tell him I like bein' in ta hills better. I'm gonna put this here artifact ina safe place. See ya, Ely."

Two minutes after Will left the store, there were people shouting in the road. I looked out to find Will and his uncle arguing, apparently, so I walked outside to see what I could do, and I heard that Joe haranguing about Will's tomahawk head.

"Why don't you take the stone to your father, a true historian, who could tell you its value? Why don't you go home . . ."

Instead of serving as peacemaker, I combated Joe's sassy words with my own thoughts. We were discussing the matter, and I was getting heated, until we noticed that Will had gone away. He was sitting on a big rock, laughing at the two of us, and that set me to laughing and silenced Joe. Without saying anything, he walked toward his house.

Then I looked to Will and thought that even in his laughter he needed some encouragement, so I said, "I've got to hand it to you, son. You've got more sense than I do—and much more sense than your uncle does. I hope you find more pieces of Indian handiwork. They'll be worth something, some day."

The next morning my two eldest children were searching for stones like Will's, and he was joining them in Devil's Kitchen. Looked as if he were questioning them, but my young ones didn't have the answers Will was looking for, evidently. There he went, heading toward his uncle's log house. I stayed as busy as I could, wanting to avoid any more heated confrontations with that Joe. Soon enough Will stepped into the store.

"Ely, I lost ta tomahawk head! Thought I put it in a good

hidin' place. Asked everyone at home if they knowed what happened ta it, but no one knowed 'bout it till Uncle Joe came last night and talked 'bout my habits. A maid heard him say somethin' 'bout my stone. Seems I got holda a bad luck rock 'cause it's already caused me more trouble than I ever knowed. My pa tells me ta forget 'bout it and just find another. But I went ta ask Uncle Joe 'bout it and he ignored ta subject, for ta most part. I'm more confused after talkin' ta him then I am before. Seems I got more then my share a trials in these hills."

Will shuffled his feet in that thoughtful, shy manner of his and all the sudden blurted out, "Oh, 'most forgot this here message from my ma. She's expectin' a crowd a folks from Kansas City."

It read,

To Mrs. Amos:

Would you be so kind as to prepare three of your exquisite, delicious sheet cakes by this weekend. Enclosed is usual payment per cake. Please send reply with my son Will. Gratefully, Mrs. Butler.

When I gave the message to Annie, she gleamed with pride, honored that Mrs. Butler would ask for her cakes again rather than have a castle servant bake some. So Annie quickly answered and handed the reply to Will. He stuck it in his pocket, ate a few candy bars, and mosied out the door.

By then there wasn't any doubt that Will was a blood member of the castle clan, but his ways were still a puzzle. That summer was the hottest I'd ever known; we managed by putting on hardly any clothes, and that was an easy adjustment for Will. He merely didn't wear a shirt under the overalls he constantly wore, didn't even shed them to go swimming. After a swim, he ran through these hills until his overalls dried, and invariably he would meet up with his uncle who'd advise him to stop acting and dressing like a hillbilly. But that boy just continued as he wished, not having an easy go of it.

Chapter IV

1928

Business picked up, causing the end of our first year in Hahatonka to pass like hounds after a rabbit. Watching birds fly south, I wandered these hills and contemplated the peacefulness of the city folks' absence. At the turn of 1928, people were coming from as far as ten miles to purchase supplies, and it was surely a welcomed change in clientele from mostly city folk messages to local folk walking right in.

The post office building was becoming a hubbub of socializing and general loitering. Talk was free and loose and gossip abundant, mostly about the clans who spent their summers in these hills. I doubt if ever anyone has been bestowed with a gift to gab equal to Pete Hinley's, and he frequented the store about as much as anyone. Not only was he driven to talk obsessively but also he was given to stretch the truth in such an artful way that few questioned his version of any story. And old Peter elaborated on several about the Butlers especially young Will.

"That one boy acts like he ain't quit right, ta way he roams ta hills talkin' to animals like he does. Why, one day I catched him near ta bottom of Whisperin' Dell shoutin' at ta top a his lungs. And ya knows that's least four hundred feet down. Thought he was ailin' till he looked up and spotted me near ta Bear Cave and he shouted, 'Why ere ya starin' at me?' 'Ere ya alright, boy?' I says ta him. Then he shouted somethin' like, 'Couldn't be better, juss testin' my voice 'gainst ta depth.' Then I pratended ta walk on but actual hid b'hind a big old oak and studied that boy. He took ta crawlin' on all fours, diggin' at the ground here and there, jumpin' from ta two caves

HAHA TONKA
POST OFFICE

down there. And I didn't dare ask him what he wasa testin' then!"

Old Pete went on and on until he had a dozen folks sitting around him, all as quiet as church mice. So I had to say something in Will's defense.

"The boy didn't grow up in these hills like we have. He approaches them differently; that's all. Why don't you give him a chance, get to know him; you might like him, might even learn something from him."

Old Pete and his listeners just chuckled at me, and from

Bear Cave in Whispering Dell

then on I only listened, though not too attentively, and kept my mouth closed. Such talk continued, almost every time a group gathered in the store, and I grew concerned about Will's welfare amidst hillbillies' scheming ways with outsiders.

* * *

Whenever the store stock was low, I drove twenty-five miles to Lebanon, the nearest trading town. It got so I was making two trips weekly with my car so I bought a truck, the wisest investment I ever made. I would buy a couple dozen chickens in these hills, load them onto the six-speed International, and drive them to town where they would sell for twice as much. I would take as many eggs as I could haul, too, and sold it all, each trip. Gas was cheap, so profit was great and, after buying stock, I would return home with extra money, not much but any amount of extra cash was a lot in those days. We were even able to put some aside for a rainy day.

And that rainy day came when Annie fell ill and needed a thyroid operation. That sickness took her close to death, but she pulled through surgery in fine shape. Then she was instructed to stay in bed for a month and not walk the stairs for at least two months, so I prepared myself for taking on two people's work.

Luckily, though, word of our shorthandedness passed through these hills with the lightning speed of any local news, and within a couple days one of Annie's cousins dropped in to offer her daughter's help for room and board. The girl was only fourteen years old but appeared stout enough to do a grown man's work, so I hired her on the spot and sent her up the stairs to check on Annie.

* * *

One day, early summer, when I was busier than a potato picker during harvest, I heard, "Got any candy bars?"

No sooner than I looked up, our hired girl was handing Will

one candy bar after another, stopping after the third one to ask, "Where you puttin' those things? I never seen a body eat candy bars like that. Ain't you had none for a while?"

Will just smiled and kept eating. Then he walked over to me, wiped his hands on his overalls, and, with the grip of a southern preacher, shook my hand.

"Good ta see ya, Ely. Much happen while I was gone?"

"Business improved quite a bit and Annie fell ill, thyroid trouble, but she's recovering just fine. She's upstairs, bet the sight of you'd be like a dose of medicine."

At that Will took off up the stairs, stayed about fifteen minutes, and came back down to tell me how much he had missed these hills and how good it was to set foot on green land, again.

That same afternoon I was hauling down toward Lebanon in my truck, carrying chickens, when out of nowhere popped up a Model T going about three miles an hour. I slammed on the brakes, pulled toward the ditch—and that sent those chickens flying. The Model T stopped, two boys jumped out, ran to my assistance, both apologizing and trying to catch the chickens.

One of the boys said, "We're learning to drive; we were going slow like our father advised. And we're ever so sorry we caused you this misfortune. We'll defray your damages."

Before I could answer, he added, "Say, isn't that the truck that sits by the post office building? Are you, by chance, Ely Amos who runs the store?"

"Yes, that's me. You must be Will's brothers."

"Hope the resemblance isn't that striking," the talkative one continued, "I'm Gus and this is Carl. We're glad to meet you. We're the two oldest Butler boys. There is one younger than Will, James, but he seldom leaves the house. We haven't avoided your store, purposely; it just seems that we do most our buying in the city and when we're here we like to shop in Lebanon. But, now that we've met you, we look forward to doing business with you."

While Gus rambled on, Carl acted as if he were preparing a statement and finally said, "Did you know our grandfather bought Hahatonka in 1904 and designed the beautiful house where we stay?"

I nodded in agreement, as he continued, "But he died two years later and never saw his dream world completed. I think about that mishap often and sometimes feel guilty that I'm not more fond of this land that our dear grandfather loved. Seems that neither his sons nor his grandchildren will continue the wonderful plans he had for Hahatonka. Will's the only one who can't wait to return here, each season, and his peculiar ways have always puzzled and concerned us anyway. As for me, if it weren't for the lovely house, I could hardly endure the summers here. That's why Gus and I are learning to drive, so we can get away occasionally."

Gus interrupted, "Don't mind Carl, Mr. Amos; he is always giving that speech when he first meets someone. He's the shy one in our family, never knows just what to talk about. We must be going. If you'll kindly send a bill for the damages to our father, we assure you that you will be paid. Again, our apologies. Good day."

Luckily the ditch wasn't too steep so I could back the truck out. I turned it around and headed back to the store, having lost the wherewithal to do any serious trading in Lebanon, all the while thinking about Will's brothers and about their attitude toward him.

Who was at the store but the one person I was least up to seeing, Pete Hinley. Even Will's uncle Joe would have been a more welcomed sight as I walked through the door, because I knew old Pete was merely instigating more gossip about Will. And, sure enough, he had a group of folks in an uproar.

They were laughing and making comments like, "That 'tarded boy's back for ta summer. We uns'll have more 'musement now!" and "His ma and pa mustn't be so 'shamed a him ta way they let him run loose!"

I was just about to demand some order and quiet when in walked Will. The noise slowly died and all eyes focused on Will. He walked to the candy bars, as if there weren't another soul except me in the store.

"Hi, Ely, think I'll juss have two today and one pop."

As he helped himself, a few snickers spread through the room, and Will calmly commented, to me, "Sounds like some folks come down with colds. Hope it don't turn to a epidemic!"

I burst into laughter and cast my eyes across the room. Folks began walking out, some with their faces toward the floor; few had nerve enough to glance at Will. But old Pete walked up to pierce a long look at Will.

"Testin' ya voice much here late, boy?"

"Nope, no need ta anymore."

Frustrated with his inability to rouse Will, old Pete strutted outside. But Will's expression was not that of a victor's.

"Ely, I don't think these folks take to me much."

"I think they simply don't understand you, son. Be patient and watch that you don't fall prey to any of their foolishness. Being accepted takes a long time, in some cases years, in these hills. But then, these hills have a way of taking care of their own, and being born in them doesn't necessarily make one a part of them. It's how you feel about these hills, not what locals say and think about you, that matters."

Tears were dripping from Will's chin as he ran outside, and I watched him continue running until the massiveness of these hills hid him from my view.

The day after that incident, a stranger walked into the store, said he was a fur trader from St. Louis where he worked for a large shipping company, wanted to know if I ever dealt in furs.

"Yes, sir, occasionally I catch some beaver, but the real hunters are farther back in these hills. I deal mostly in chickens and eggs."

"Mr. Amos, we've need of goods, fresh goods, from this area, and you seem in an ideal situation to trade with us. If you would serve as our mediate representative, between us and your local people, we'll see that you are generously rewarded. Here's my card. I'll be back this way in a month and I'll be looking forward to discussing trade terms with you then."

Certainly he was a businessman because not a wasteful

word, small talk, was said during the fifteen minute meeting. And I felt like a full pledged businessman, myself, after he left, though no transactions had taken place. Despite my previous trading experiences, I'd never felt like a true businessman, so I attributed the feeling that day to the St. Louis man's attitude. It represented what I'd always thought the business mind should reflect—confidence, courtesy, directness, and conscientiousness—so I finally had an opportunity to practice, to respond to, what I'd only been able to theorize, until that day.

Later I was thinking about that, again, while I sat above the lake, letting the cool evening breeze soothe my body. All the sudden I heard piano music, ragtime, coming from the log house. It was pretty, so I lay back to listen more attentively, when Annie came to my side.

"Since I'm finally able to exercise, let's go for a walk."

We took off up the road, strolling all the way to the natural bridge turn off, where we'd seen several cars turn. Since that was the only entrance, by road, to the castle, we figured there was going to be some activity up there that evening. But it didn't concern us in any way, so we went to the bridge and looked over the sinkhole. That set us into a romantic mood, and I led Annie under the bridge. We spent a full hour there, completely undisturbed. Though many others considered the natural bridge their own, private hideaway, we knew it was entirely ours from then on.

By the time we returned home, our hired girl had put all the young ones to bed, but no one was asleep because that ragtime was still filling the air. It was pleasant when we had heard it a fourth mile up the road, but it began grating our nerves as we undressed for bed, then had us shaking as we lay, open-eyed, in bed.

It was too warm to close any windows but we did anyway and kept them closed until our sweat made the beds wet. As we opened the windows, we heard new, rollicking sounds, jovial party voices, a dozen or more folks dancing in the road.

Seems the castle activities overflowed to the log house or

Natural Bridge

perhaps Joe and his wife were just having one of their usual parties. Whatever, the celebration was out of control, and we were unwillingly involved. Knowing we couldn't just barge onto the road and demand quiet, we decided to sit it out and approach Joe when the timing was right. It was 2:30 a.m. before either our senses were numbed or the party ended.

What little money we gave our hired girl she'd spent on a phonograph, and she was playing it that morning after chores. In no time, with his eyes half opened and his face as white as a sheep, that Joe came into the store to announce his complaints.

"The noise coming from your house is disturbing my family's sleep, and we were up very late last night. Could you please be more quiet."

I looked up from my paper work to explain, "It's way into daylight, the time working folks are busy, and in the middle of the night OUR sleep was disturbed by your loud party! I don't feel obliged to turn down the music. Anyway, I can hardly hear it from here; surely it's not keeping you folks awake! If you'll kindly excuse me. I have WORK to do!"

At that, Joe said nothing, just rushed out of the store. My biggest concern was the front door, the abuse it was getting that summer. I suspected I'd have to order a new one soon.

Thank goodness not many folks came into the store that day, save the regulars to check on their mail. Ida Maines had to give her weather report, as usual, when she asked for her mail, and old Pete Hinley peeked in to try striking up conversation; both those folks got little response from me that day, so they left shortly after they came. I was never so glad to see the end of a business day in all my years. Just as I was locking up, Will came in.

"A couple candy bars for ta road. Summer's gone, so I'll be goin' back ta Kansas City. Maybe that's where I should stay, but I'll probably see ya next summer. So long, Ely."

I had barely enough time to say, "Good-bye; good luck in your school work!" before Will rushed away, but I noticed he went in the opposite direction of the castle.

Five minutes later Will's brother Gus drove up, jumped out of his Model T, and banged on the store door.

Before I opened the door, he shouted, "Have you seen Will? We're all waiting for him."

"Yes, he went that way," I said, as I reached the door and pointed up the road.

Gus took off like lightning, and I started a new kind of concern about Will, thinking that perhaps he needed a break from these hills.

Chapter V

1929

As autumn approached, our hired girl was growing homesick, too homesick to stay with us, so we sent her on her way. How anxious we were for winter, for snow to cover these hills, mostly because it would have meant our vacation from all those city folks; and, at the very moment Annie and I were discussing that, who walked into the store but Joe, parading in a sporty zoot suit as if he were ready for another party.

"My mail, please, as soon as possible."

"We do what we can as quickly as we can. You have no mail," I retorted, wondering why his children weren't in school.

Whatever their reason, that Joe and his clan were there, living it up, while my clan and I were worried we'd never again know a quiet night.

Joe had two little girls, each cuter than the other, and they often busied themselves outdoors, even joined our young ones in play whenever it was convenient to do so. One day I heard some awful screaming, looked out, and there was Joe's younger girl hanging upside-down from a tree and my oldest was laughing so hard she could hardly stand up. I must say, the sight brought on a chuckle, but I straightened up and went out to grab hold of the situation, just in time to meet up with Joe. And, as he stood there shaking his head in puzzlement, his wife strolled onto the scene.

"Look what your roughneck child did to my civilized daughter, Mr. Amos! Perhaps I should ban your children from this side of the road, for their ways are too rough an influence on my daughters. Would you kindly see to it that your, your children play with children more their style!"

During that fiery speech, Joe continued shaking his head and untied his little girl. As his wife pranced back to her house, Joe merely attempted to soothe over the incident.

"The sight upset my wife so much that I'm afraid she spoke too harshly, irrationally. I'm sorry. Good day."

There was no chance of talking to a temperament such as Joe's wife's, but Joe's reaction impressed me and had me thinking I might have jumped to some wrong conclusions about him in the past. But I had a feeling that that incident would have later repercussions.

Just as the St. Louis businessman had said, he returned in a month, and there he stood, waiting to discuss business, while I was wanting to rehash my young one's experience. But business came first, and especially in those days; that was the way it had to be, so I sent my young one upstairs to await the inevitable talk.

"Have you any furs, Mr. Amos, by chance, so early in the season?"

"Sir, not yet, but I've plenty chickens and eggs to do some healthy trading. Maybe we could settle price now and later I could ship you the furs."

He liked my proposal, and within ten minutes we were business partners. That meeting initiated shipping that continued to provide a steady, though slight, income throughout our stay in Hahatonka.

Thanksgiving came and finally we were rid of our troublesome neighbors, and that holiday was celebrated in a high way. It well could have been my imagination, but it seemed these hills took on a more restful, relaxed tint the day all the city folks were gone. But snow was yet to fall.

Also Thanksgiving marked the seasonal closing of the restaurant that stood near the Big Spring. The proprietors of that restaurant patronized our store, so when they closed doors for the winter, I made fewer trips to Lebanon. With that and the fact that winter meant fewer tourists, as 1929 rolled around, we began closing the store on Sundays.

With each season Hahatonka took on an entirely different

face. Winter was our favorite, though not our most active, for then these hills acquired a glow of supremacy that wasn't so noticeable during other seasons. In winter little detracted from these hills; even the usual snow merely heightened their splendor by adding an appearance of purity. But, despite all its glory, winter kept a relation with other seasons in that local folks still held their occasional gatherings in the store.

Common to the hillbilly was (and has always been) the somewhat dangerous trait of exaggerating, having the imagination's trigger pulled, once he finally starts talking. And, though old Pete Hinley might have taken the care for that, there were others almost as gifted. When they joined forces, always there was sufficient fuel for stories, most of them outrageous. That old potbellied stove served as nucleus for many a bull session, and that particular winter it stood in the center of a most flagrant instigation. Of course, old Pete started the ball rolling.

"With folks gone outa ta castle, it ain't any too safe; I know 'cause I seen things flyin' 'round it last night, things looked like bats or somethin'. No tellin' what those city folks left behind here. Far all we uns know, some ghosts!"

"Maybe that 'tarded boy has friends a guardin' his big home while he gone away."

"Nah, that boy lives most in the hills where critters take ta him. Must be somethin' else hangin' out in that castle."

"Like Pete here says, maybe there's ghosts hidin' out up there, perfec' place for 'em."

"Seems we uns oughta have a looksee, when it gets warmer weather. In the meantime, we should all keep a watchout. Ya don't know that if there's ghosts up there but what they won't start ta spreadin' out further and 'fore we know it, we'll have ourselves ghosts all over."

Then old Pete concluded, "Good thinkin', we'll take turns checkin' and watchin' ta castle each evenin'. While it's so cold, that's 'bout all we uns can do. All us settin' right here will look out one night a week. I'll go checkin 't'night."

Pete could hardly wait to finish one story so that he could begin another.

THE OLD MILL, HAHATONKA, MO.

"Now, did ya all hear 'bout what old Butler, ta head one, the wild boy's pa, did 'fore he left here? Let me tell ya. He reopened ta old grist mill, had hired help run it, twice already 'fore school started up. Why, guess he thinks he's doin' local folk a favor. Half ta turn of corn ya take in ta worker keeps as pay. So your grain adds up ta less then that, hardly ain't worth ta trip. But I 'spect plenty folk'll keep ta old mill busy."

A gentle, elderly gentleman spoke up, "I feel it's a fine service, what Mr. Butler's doin' with the old grist mill, and I hear tell from hired help that Trout Glen is goin' be opened late this spring. I'm lookin' forward ta catchin' me some trout there. That's mighty nice of ta estate, openin' up ta land like that."

Pete had to finish that story, too, "Yah, well, there's profits in it far him, or he would't be doin' it. I'll bet any 'mount on that. No city man goin' come out here and help us in any way. Gettin' dark; best be goin'."

With that, others mossied out, too, and I must say, I was always glad to see Pete's group leave the store.

* * *

By mid-February, later in the winter than usual, these hills looked like big balls of cotton, unused and sanitary. As beautiful as it was, the snow made it pretty difficult for folks to get around. Some of Pete's lookout group couldn't meet their schedules of watching the castle, and, though that made their sessions around the potbellied stove less lively, it wasn't long until another topic filled the store with plenty idle talk and frail concern.

Mr. Hatch, a man of reputable, estimable character, the Butler Estate foreman, shared word with old Pete that things were going to change at Hahatonka, that some electric company was planning to build a dam on the river. I'd never heard old Pete speak so seriously.

"Why, a power dam ta size they're a talkin' 'bout would change ta whole 'plexion of ta land. It'd make a big lake out there where ta Niangua and ta Osage meet, not ta tell how it'd make water back up somethin' awful, cover crops and eve' houses. Why, water'd cover halfa what we uns see 'round us right now. It'd be a cryin' shame, a cryin' shame."

"Sure as hell old Butler won't let that happen ta his land!"

"We're settin' awful low ta that bottom a the hills, water could take all our belongin's."

"Me and mine juss got settled into ma grandpapie's place; we waited mighty long ta live there, and it stands awful far down in a valley."

"Ta good Lord won't let some gush a water juss come over us, least ways, without warnin'. We'll have ta wait ta see if it happens; then pray ta high heavens we can all keep our homes and crops."

After the hysterical surmising, which included the voice of everyone sitting around the stove, a silence crept over the store as if the reality of the sad possibility had struck us all at once and no one had a verbal defense against it. For the second time, I witnessed Pete's group silently leave the store, that time with their faces longer than before.

We all waited out winter to hear further word from the Butler Estate. Though fairly convinced that the ghosts, bats, or whatever, were creatures of pure imagination, still, and religiously as the weather grew warmer, members of Pete's group took their turns watching the castle. And one early spring evening one of them came hauling up the road, hopped out of his truck before it'd hardly stopped, and ran into the store to announce that he'd seen the head Mr. Butler driving onto Hahatonka.

"Now we uns can find out 'bout ta dam, for sure. If nothin' else, Hatch will know more 'bout it now, and he'll pass it on ta us," old Pete mumbled.

Mr. Hatch was a busy man, managing what'd grown to be over five thousand acres and supervising a dozen workers year around. But once in a while we could see him joy riding one of the estate's horses. That man loved to ride horses, never saw him in a car. And the very moment old Pete was mumbling about finding the truth about the dam, we heard the gallop of a horse coming up the road. In walked Mr. Hatch, solemn and hurried.

"Ely, may I have some soap and a good size brush for the horse. He's been driving so hard lately; I'd like to reward him with some private pampering. He's a find old critter."

That was more than I'd ever heard Mr. Hatch talk in one breath, almost sounded like pure nervousness. I obliged him best I could and then motioned to old Pete not to bother Mr. Hatch. But, though Pete had his good points, he could never stifle his curiosity.

"Hatch, have ya talked ta Butler since he's back? We're all 'bout ta bust not knowin' if our land goin' dispere or what. We're countin' on ya ta 'vise us if ya know somethin'."

"Well, Pete, it don't look too promisin'. I think that's why Mr. Butler came back so soon, and the man's health is failing here lately, so I don't push any issues with him. We'll all just have to fight for what we got. I know that's what he'll do if anybody threatens his land. Seems he wants to get a grip on things before his family comes down here; he wants to be alone."

Old Pete seemed to settle for that, and the rest of us nodded in agreement. Mr. Hatch left as hurriedly as he'd entered. And from that moment on, the store took on an atmosphere that's difficult to describe; certainly there was less imaginative talk around the potbellied stove, and the issue of ghosts became a matter worthless of mention.

It wasn't long after that that Joe returned, too, without his clan. Seems the two brothers were sharing a terrible, heavy burden. Twice, while I was out hunting food, I saw them on the natural bridge, just gazing over their land as if they were waiting for it to vanish before their eyes. Both times, when I saw their expressions, I felt as if a rock dropped from my throat to my stomach.

* * *

One day Joe got his car stuck in a ditch down the road. It was raining something awful, and, because I had that 6-speed International, I was called to help. After I hitched his car to my truck, pulled it out, got him back onto the road, Joe didn't say a word. So I drove back to the store, thinking what an ingrate he was. That next morning there was an envelope lying on the floor, inside the store door.

A note in it read, "Mr. Amos, thank you. I was most grateful for your able assistance. Joe Butler."

Also inside the envelope was a ten dollar bill, and I began wondering how else I had misjudged that Joe.

* * *

Will looked older when he walked into the store that summer, but he talked the same.

"Ely, I've been learnin' a lot by hangin' 'round Mr. Hatch. That man knows how ta fix anythin' needin' some repair. Yesterday I watched him mend that pump at ta grist mill, ta hydrolic gimmick that sends water ta tha tower. He did it like he knowed all 'bout such a machine. Taday I'm goin' learn 'bout handlin' a horse. Gosh, I need a pop. I'm workin' up a powerful sweat, and those candy bars look better then ever."

"Will, is your whole clan back?"

"Yep, and so is Uncle Joe's. We're all worried over what's goin' be built on ta river, that dam they call it. Some power company's givin' my pa a awful hard time. He's too good a man ta be bothered like that. I'd like ta tell those company folks a thin' or two. Eve' Uncle Joe's upset. I heared some tree cutters are comin' soon. Pa spends halfa his time talkin' ta law folks, and he's gettin' sicker by ta day. Sure do wish they'd leave him 'lone."

I tried to console young Will, but he was beyond any condescending talk by them. I realized I was speaking with a young man, who, except receiving another D grade in English, had made all perfect marks again in school.

* * *

Mr. Hatch had a helper who was an ace at operating that old mill. Every Saturday, beginning early spring, there was a line of farmers, holding their turns of corn, and Pete's group no longer criticized the grist mill's purposes.

One Saturday Will was right in the center of the entire works, and a couple hillbillies were ribbing him about his overgrown size, while old Pete, though quiet for a change, stood in line and smiled at the entertainment. Will began helping the mill operator and ignored the snide remarks; then a booming voice sounded from near the water tower, a voice singing in a way that local folks weren't accustomed to hearing.

The sound fell to the mill area with such an impact that all the folks there reacted. Some of them giggled and whispered to each other as if the singing were a hoax for their own benefit; some ducked their heads as if the sky were going to drop; some shyly left the mill and headed homeward.

While he continued working, Will said to me, "That's my uncle Joe; he sings opera music, pretty, ain't it!"

After a couple minutes, it did grow pleasing to the ear, but still most of the folks hanging around the mill were sure the sky was going to fall. They all became quiet and began listening.

That night I heard a group of voices shouting, "Joe, Joe, come out and sing!"

I looked out in time to see Joe walking outside his log house, stand on the porch, and start singing. After an opera song, one of the folks, the same young worker who'd been at the mill that afternoon, who seemed to take a special liking to Joe, requested a particular country tune, and Joe sang it with the same gusto that he'd sung his own kind of music. His voice was captivating; he sang like a professional, like a man who knew everything about music and felt it with his soul. Folks gathered from all sides and soon packed the road for a block, a country block.

Since we continued closing the store on Sundays, my clan and I habitually spent that day in leisure, usually swimming and picnicking. And that Sunday, the day after we'd learned Joe could sing so beautifully, Annie, our young ones, and I hiked down to Hahatonka Lake. As usual, we carried fried chicken with us and planned to swim before we were to eat.

By the time we returned to our picnic spot, the chicken was gone. No one else was in sight. Then along came Will, Mr. Hatch, and some of his clan. They were toting enough chicken to feed an army, so we accepted their invitation to join them.

We laughed, told stories, and lounged in the comfort of these splendid hills until they completely hid the sunlight. We parted in good spirits, never having mentioned the rumor about that dam being built.

Walking up the road, we saw groups of men, rugged looking folks, setting up camp by the restaurant. Nodding in their direction, we kept walking, wondering if possibly they were there to begin work for the electric company that wanted to change these hills.

One of the men whistled at Annie and we heard, "Hey, look at ta pretty hills lady," and I thought Annie was going to faint from embarrassment.

I was angry, looked in the direction of their camp, only to see several dozen men scurrying around as if they were frantically building their own little town. Then I didn't consider them a direct threat to Annie but felt a strangely corrupt and bitter attitude in their manners.

When we reached the hilltop, we looked across the lake toward the castle and pondered its beauty, its growing meaning as a landmark in these hills.

"Even if the water backs up, Ely, at least, it won't reach the castle; for some reason, that's a consolation to me," Annie whispered.

Sometimes a soul had to stand in pure awe of the sight we had from the storefront, and that's just what we did, many times, that evening being one particular time. Before we knew it, night had come and even the log house looked peacefully retired, its inhabitants quiet. The only sound was that of those men still setting up camp.

That next day the store was bustling with those campers ordering everything from axes to coal oil lamps. They bought out our entire stock of such items, and I was listing what all I needed to pick up in Lebanon. In the midst of that commotion,

I felt an awful, sudden pain in my hip; I could hardly move. The campers continued shopping and browsing while Annie worked the counter.

Will walked in, went to the candy bar counter and stood bewilderingly.

"No more candy bars, and I sure was needin' some. Why, there ain't no candy a'tall. What happened, Ely, and why ya settin' there like that with all this business?

"Son, I want you to find Mr. Hatch; I need him to look at my hip. With the pain I'm having, I can't travel to a doctor."

At that, Will ran out faster than lightning, followed by some bad remarks about his size and ways. In no time, in walked Mr. Hatch, and all he conjectured was that I stay still, in bed, until I could make it to see a doctor.

A week passed, and I still couldn't walk. During that time, those campers were frequenting the store and turning Annie into a nervous wreck. Never at a loss of topics for dirty jokes and with their faces darkened by something, possibly their work, they paraded in to demand supplies. They made Pete and his group a welcomed bunch, welcomed customers.

Annie managed to hitch a ride to Springfield, seventy-five miles away, just to buy a large supply of axes. Knowing she'd be on the road a full day, she arranged for a local man to operate the store and asked Will to help out. Annie returned with three dozen axes, a week's supply. It was hard to tell what thirty-five to forty men did with so many axes.

Cash was scarce so most bills were paid the end of the month or whenever workers were paid. That applied to everyone in and around Hahatonka. Even the Butlers were sent a bill, on a tri-monthly basis, and we received payment shortly thereafter. But, since the store building was owned by the Butlers, as was every other building in Hahatonka, rent, twenty dollars a month, was subtracted from their bill. Business terms were as simple as possible in those days, and we always looked forward to receiving sizable payments such as the one we were expecting for the axes.

* * *

Soon there was no doubt in anyone's mind why those campers came to Hahatonka, as the sound of saws, buzzing, could be heard for miles. Lying in bed with nothing except my senses functioning, it seemed as if any sound were directed solely toward me. And that buzzing told me the peaceful, calm, easy days in Hahatonka were over. When I heard trees falling, I felt pieces of these hills fade, harshly, into my mind's memory.

A doctor stopped, passing through to Lebanon, so Annie sent him upstairs to examine my hip. He diagnosed the problem as rheumatism and advised me to stay in bed until the pain ceased. That I did. In a few days, I was walking around like normal, and the disappearance of pain put new color in my cheeks while my returning to operate the store put Annie back to her normal self—almost.

A dark cloud moved closer to our lives as more trees fell, day by day, threatening our very actions. Even Will's usual, easy manner forsook him to become a token victim of the falling trees' onslaught, and it was detectable to everyone, causing the likes of Pete Hinley to ease up on Will. The second day that I was on my feet, Will entered the store to drink some soda and, of course, to eat some candy bars.

"Ely, that stinkin' sound of them buzzin' saws is a followin' me ev'where I go and I don't know a remedy. Looks like ya found a remedy for your hip, good seein' ya up and 'round. . . . Wish more then anythin' somethin' could be done 'bout those outlaws! That's what they ere, ya know, plain bandits—comin' in here destroyin' OUR land, tryin' us!"

While Will and I stood contemplating what he'd just said, in walked old Pete to announce, "Campers, them wood cutters, walkin' all over; here comes two a them now, tough lookin' men."

The three of us gazed out the store window to see tree cutters marching up the road, a frightening sight. They appeared jolly, cocky—and dirty. Pete, Will and I each sighed as they continued walking, past the store, carrying their axes like rifles under their arms; and we wondered where they were headed, what part of these hills they were going to attack next.

Old Pete broke the silence by asking, "Boy, ya been swimmin' here late? Ain't seen much a ya since ta day ya was helpin' at ta mill."

Will hesitated, probably to ponder just why old Pete decided to talk civilly, then replied, "Swim when I got time; been hikin' a lot, lookin' over ta land, findin' where those. . . . Been nice weather, ain't it? Good weather for doin' most anythin'."

My heart began aching for that boy. There was such pain and sorrow in his voice; even his walk seemed different; he paced his steps, almost as if measuring them, out the door. Pete looked to me and shook his head in simple sympathy. Then we saw Joe leave his house, meet up with Will, and put his arm around the boy, the two of them posing a sharp contrast to the previous partners who'd just paraded the opposite direction.

* * *

In the heat of summer, Hahatonka Lake continually hosted bathers, boaters, and fishermen, and among those sportsmen was Joe's wife. One day we heard a fearsome scream from someone on the water. I ran behind the log house to see Joe's wife struggling toward a canoe that Mr. Hatch's young helper was steering. He was attempting to keep that canoe straight up while reaching for Joe's wife. By the time I made it to the water, he'd pulled her into the boat, and I couldn't help but laugh at the sight of that overbearing woman as helpless as a drowning baby. It looked as if she couldn't swim and was relying on that helper to save her. After she made it back into the boat, she began raving about her hair, how it had just been styled for a party that night. The helper was doing all he could to hold back his laughter, but finally he burst into a roaring fit. Then, to my surprise, and I wouldn't have believed it second-hand, that lady saw humor in the situation, too, and laughed so hard that she practically tipped the canoe again.

That evening there was a party, all right, and Annie and I

knew we were bound to be up until wee hours. So we prepared by throwing our own get-together in the store. Old Pete and his group attended, Will showed his face several times, and about twenty-five other local folks joined in the merriment. It was a grand night, and not one person mentioned the threat hanging over these hills.

But that next day was a most sad one. Mr. Hatch's wife died, spreading a grief that fit right into the real atmosphere. Will brought the news to the store, and from there it traveled through these hills.

That funeral brought together most of the local folks, including the Butlers, not only to mourn a death but also to homogeneously hear those buzzing saws. Very few grievers lasted the entire service, and I was one that didn't, couldn't. I waited outside with those who had been either crying so hard they disrupted the service or grieving so bad they couldn't sit any longer. The charades of all us folks surrounding a corpse amidst the sounds of these hills falling, piece by piece, was more than most of us could handle. It was almost as if the sound of those buzzing saws was coming from Mrs. Hatch's corpse, telling us that our misery was only beginning. It was a pitiful affair.

Then, heading for the burial grounds, our procession passed the woodcutters' camp, and a glad note struck my heart for Mrs. Hatch, as I realized she had been the last to see her homeland in tact.

* * *

Will wasn't frequenting the store, and that made me wonder where he was spending his time. Not being taken to labor, it was a sure bet he wasn't working for anyone, yet he was doing something time-consuming. Just as I was thinking about him, into the store he came.

"Ely, ya know that cave inside ta island? Well, I was in it yesterday and mosta t'day, a good place ta think, to ponder what's goin' on 'round here. I heard strange sounds in there—

but no trees a fallin' and no saws a goin'. I made believe time was standin' still and I wasn't bein' tried by nothin'. But somethin', maybe time itself, ta time inside my senses, broke my dream and I realized stayin' in ta cave wasn't gettin' me nowheres. So I left ta cave ta do some investigatin', ta see juss what they're a doin' ta our hills. As I saw, a sadness come or me that put tears in my eyes, more then at Mrs. Hatch's funeral, and I started a screamin' at those tree-cutters—everone I could find. They ignored me, some laughed and poked fun—but all them juss kept sawin' 'way. There got ta be some tactics ta stop em. That's what my pa is a workin' on, but his health's still goin' down. And we's all worried 'bout him, more then before. Well, that's what I was a doin', anyways. Now I'm goin' go try ta listen ta them lawyers talk with pa and Uncle Joe. Once 'fore I did that; couldn't make heads or tails a what they said, but I figure if I keep a listenin', I'll catch on. Just a couple candy bars today, Ely. Gota run!"

* * *

The fish trapping, where the lake and spring connected, was going strong. The estate gained over five hundred dollars a month just by shipping those crawfish to restaurants, mostly in St. Louis. It took several hired helpers about five hours a day to operate the barrel traps and transfer the caught fish into wooden shipping boxes. A thriving business that was, and Mr. Hatch ran it as well as he ran all the estate work.

Our sympathy went to that man. His wife left him with ten children to care for. They lived next to us in what was always called the brown house, a house built to room castle workers. Annie did all she could to help watch after all his young ones, and luckily there were a couple Hatch children old enough to fill parts of the role their mother had left. Amidst all attempts to hold that family together, it was Mr. Hatch's strength, his ability to carry on, that spirited his entire clan.

Our three young ones, hired helper, and I standing on crawfish shipping crates. Picture taken by Annie.

He was an inspiration to us all. Still our hearts pleaded for him, as his hurt and pain was clearly noticeable sometimes.

On one of those hot, noisy afternoons. I was heading toward Lebanon to trade and buy stock when I saw Will on his hands and knees in Devil's Kitchen. Figuring he was just searching for more artifacts, I kept on driving. Then I saw Joe, with something like a stone in his hand, walking toward Will. It seemed those two were getting along better and better, and that thought gave me a happy feeling as I drove down the road.

For the second time, Will's two older brothers pulled out in front of me on that same road. But that time they didn't cause my load of chickens and eggs to fly off. Rather they pulled over, waving as if I were the only person they'd seen in months, and let me pass them. Perhaps they were warning me of the oncoming wagon and horses—that I hadn't seen soon enough. Into the ditch that old 6-speed International went again!

"Can we help you, Mr. Amos?" I heard, as the team of horses and their wagon flew on by.

There were Carl and Gus, ready to pitch in again to help me reload the truck, and that time I was especially grateful to them.

"Mighty kind of you boys," I said, as we were catching chickens.

"Are you all right, Mr. Amos?" Gus asked.

"Yes, thank you. Say, boys, I'd appreciate it if you'd tell me whenever you gas up your cars at the store. I don't see you every time, and I need to know so that I can add the charge to your father's bill."

"Sure, Mr. Amos; we'd assumed someone kept an eye on that gas tank. From now on, we'll let you know each time we fill up a car. . . . Sure is a hot day. I think we'll go for a swim and let you get on your way. Good to see you again, Mr. Amos."

When I returned from Lebanon, Will was delivering another request for more cakes from his mother. Annie was more and more honored that she was chosen above castle maids and cooks to prepare cakes for Mrs. Butler's special occasions, and that time she was to bake nine sheet cakes in two days. Luckily we always had the needed ingredients in stock as sugar and flour and such were in demand, constantly.

"Say, Will, what were you searching for earlier today in Devil's Kitchen? More artifacts?" I asked, while he devoured several candy bars.

"Matter a fact, Ely, that's exactly what I was doin'. Then, of all surprises, Uncle Joe found one far me, said it was one he found a while back. It looked a whole lot like ta one I lost, but he said somethin' like, 'This was located near our own house, and I thought ya might be interested in havin' it.' So I took it with many thanks. Awful nice a my uncle ta think a me that way. I'm thinkin' I never knowed him up till recent. I never gave him much a chance ta make sense ta me. I juss thought he was always funnin' and makin' fun a me, but I think he's got a big heart. Seems he even talks different ta me, these days. Could be juss me, my need ta hear him make sense. Anyways, Ely, did ya hear 'bout ta law suit my folks are makin' 'gainst that power company? We're goin' fight em from makin' water cover our land. Cross ya fingers, Ely."

Before I could answer Will, old Pete walked in and said, in his customary, loud voice, "Heard what ya folks a doin' ta fight that damned power company, boy. Maybe we'll lick em still, even d'spite trees fallin' more ever day. Everbody's b'hind ya folks, boy. Ya tell em that!"

I don't know which of us, Will or I, was more shocked by Pete's kind remark.

As he left the store, Will simply replied, "Thank ya, Mr. Hinley; that'll mean a lot ta my pa and my uncle."

Some of Pete's regular group came in shortly after that, and, though not burning coal, the potbellied stove once again served as the center of a bull session, a less nonsensical gathering than most were. Their talk was unusually low, tamed, and direct.

"We'll juss have ta hang on in there and when and if we're approached by some member of that company, we'll tell em we're not a budgin'."

"Maybe they'll never come ta us; maybe we uns be safe after all. Maybe ta Butlers can keep em 'way far us all!"

"Yal, they's a tryin' awful hard. Who uns ever think local folk be a backin' em city intruders? Ha, now they's ta only folk with enough drive ta do what can save us all. Almost tickles ya funny bone."

Talk continued, soaring to serious planes that I hadn't thought were even possible within that group. I guess we all were changing, somewhat, in the face of such a threat to our homes and livelihoods.

Chapter VI

1930

That autumn the Butler clans' recess to the city was not made in the customarily conspicuous fashion, and it didn't effect the usual, cheerful feeling amongst local folks. If it weren't for Will having stopped to say goodbye, we wouldn't have known they were leaving. No one seemed to anticipate any freedom or relief in Butlers' return to the city. Surprising how one's feelings for folks could change because of circumstances around them; seeing folks cope with different situations surely did effect Annie and me, and it seemed to put a change in many local folks.

The old schoolhouse bell began ringing again in the mornings, and, since the schoolmaster was boarding upstairs the store with us, he accompanied our school aged young one almost every morning. About forty children attended that school, and the schoolmaster had his hands full. None of us expected him to last the entire school year, but he did. Also when that bell rang, other daily activities began—the restaurant doors opened, saws started buzzing, and folks began strolling into the store.

One morning Mr. Butler, who stayed in these hills that autumn with his brother Joe, walked in to make certain his bills were squared away. A man of few words, he barely explained his purpose in being there, while he gazed over the merchandise.

"Mr. Amos, you keep a good, well organized store. If I had more time, I would trade here instead of sending my employees to shop for me. As it is, though, I hardly ever do the ordering for estate needs. But I do want you to know that it is a pleasure doing business with you when I can. Blessings to you and your family. Good day."

All that he said in one breath while taking two steps to reach the door. The more I saw him the more I realized how his and Will's appearances were very similar; both stood over six feet, five inches and walked liked gorillas, like their arms were doing all the work in moving their bodies; neither was endowed with the Butlers' good looks, but then both possessed a peculiar manner that marked them as Butler men, a gentle, hearty, strong character. Somehow I felt, especially after seeing a picture of Will's grandfather, that Will was more a direct descendant of the castle designer's character than were any of the other Butlers. I'd thought that, too, of Will's father before his health began failing and he became more dependent. Still he and Will seemed brothers in their mannerisms and attitudes especially as Will grew older before my very eyes.

* * *

One crisp day, Annie and her cousin were invited on a coon hunt, a wild adventure for anyone who'd never before ventured into these hills for that reason. Business was particularly slow that day, so I told Annie to go out and enjoy herself, since she'd always wondered what a "coon hunt" was like, and I'd tend her post office duties. By evening Annie was still out. Night came and her cousin's husband came to the store. We decided to go searching for the two ladies.

"Annie!" "Wilma!" we shouted in these hills until we became hoarse.

Resting our bones above Whispering Dell, we heard faint screams coming closer and closer. Surely enough, Annie and Wilma were climbing up the hill, behind us, their dresses torn and their faces full of fear.

"We've been walking at least three miles, long before River Cave! Those mean men left us, saying they had to walk over the next hill crest by themselves but that they'd return for us. After an hour or so. . . ." Annie cried out, unable to continue talking, she was crying so hard.

Beginning of Hahatonka (Big) Spring.

Big Spring at Trout Glen, right of island and bottom of castle cliff.

Big Spring along the spring path, left of island.

I consoled her as best I could, halfway chuckling at the entire ordeal, knowing it was only a prank and that the outing did her more good than a day in the store would have. We slowly walked toward home while Annie's cousin and her husband went their respective way. Annie didn't simmer down until she was fast asleep in bed.

The next day was Sunday, our family's special day together. Though Annie wasn't too keen on taking a walk, she was convinced by our young ones that we all should go down to the island. We hiked the spring path by the restaurant, that looked more forsaken than ever, and continued toward the old mill. Clearly we saw that the water had risen almost over the dam, and we shakily crossed to the island. Reaching the top of the island, we saw that the Osage River had risen, causing the Niangua to back up into Hahatonka Lake, so that explained why the mill dam was almost flooded. After looking over these beautiful hills, yet barely being able to see some of the familiar lower planes, we journeyed back down the island and went into the cave.

At its opening there were ten to twelve lanterns, axes, and spikes. Annie, our eldest young one, and I each picked up a lantern so that we could make our way farther into the cave. We were so used to being in there that we didn't think once about encountering anything new, inside. All the sudden, our youngest screamed at the top of his lungs. I looked down to see him pointing to a mask of some sort; it'd have scared me, too, had it been hanging at my eye level. Annie picked up our young one, and I picked up the mask.

It looked like an explorer's helmet with added face protection, ugly piece of equipment. I tossed it aside and felt a threat similar to that which those buzzing saws caused. All our faces drooped, and we automatically turned around to leave the cave. Seemed some representative part of that power company's awful plan ran interference to even the most unsuspecting, carefree moments.

That same week a group of those woodcutters came into the store and took on Pete's group in ornery talk.

"Why don't ya oltimers get busy packin' ya goods far gettin' outa these parts. Water's goin' flush out what ya don't ship out."

Old Pete retorted, "You's disposition as goddarn ugly and mean as ya looks. No thinkin' twice that all ya's know how ta do is swing an axe. Talk 'mongst yaselves. We uns don't wanta hear ya yappin'."

That one woodcutter almost swung his fist at old Peter, but some of the others held him back. Pete's group took on their silent pose and just stared at the woodcutters, waiting for them to make the next comment.

"Ha, these billies don't know nothin'," was the final remark as the woodcutters grabbed some chewing tobacco and stormed out of the store.

As the last one left, the door hinges gave way, finally. I wished it would have been by anyone else's force, a local folk's.

* * *

Weeks passed to the sound of those saws buzzing and to the sight of trees falling by the dozens. Thanksgiving arrived and found the restaurant long closed. Folks, even tourists, didn't bother to get so close to the woodcutters' camp, so the restaurant lost customers, causing considerable damage to our business, for, as I mentioned earlier, the store heavily relied on the restaurant's patronage. That Thanksgiving the face of Hahatonka looked sadder than it ever had.

* * *

In the log house there was a room that had lights on, almost every other night, until wee hours in the morning. While sometimes that made me think Joe and his brother were planning, keeping an upper hand against that power company, still other times it caused a certain fear, a feeling that future existence was not at all secure.

One morning I rose in time to see that light go out, and I thought how worn and tired the two Butler men must be. Then I saw their shadows move across the walls and all my feelings were somehow reinforced by the realization that the men truly were up working all those hours. I went out to feed the chickens as Mr. Butler walked up the road. He waved one of his long arms at me as if he were really glad to see me.

To the southeast, behind our home, was a pen for hogs and a few cows. That morning I discovered that someone had broken the fence during the night. I was about to scream and shout when I noticed a note stuck to a piece of wire. It read, "Ya hillbillies shouldn't pen up critters like this. A warning." That's all it said. Immediate sensations told me it was those tree cutters, intimidating local folks again.

Then I went to the little house behind Hatch's house to ask those neighbors if they had seen anyone prowling during the night. I woke them up only to find that they hadn't heard or seen a soul. And there weren't any recognizable tracks. I was upset and worried that that one old bossy would be missing for days, if not forever. She was ready to deliver a calf, but I hadn't found time to separate her from the rest so that she'd have peace during labor. Since she'd left to find her own cubby-hole, all I could do was hope that she would return.

The old schoolhouse bell began ringing, and young ones could be seen floating, from all directions, over these hills. For that instance, these hills took on their regular, familiar atmosphere. The bell stopped ringing, the schoolhouse door closed, and those darn buzzing saws replaced the silence. I went to the store.

Folks were taking to seating themselves on top the counters that stood about four feet away from each side wall. And that day old Pete and his group gathered early. There they were, posed on the counters, when I walked in.

"Morning, Ely! Weather's better then anythin' or anybody t'day. Looks like we uns better be talkin' 'bout our futures. More trees fallin' 'round us by ta day. And water's climbin' higher then its ever been. I figure we uns in trouble, terble trouble."

Another continued, "Yep, it's all gone too darn far. That crazy Butler boy could see it even 'fore he left for ta city—and he ain't zactly ta brightest mind 'round here. We uns should be able ta see more then that boy can. But what we gonna do?"

Old Pete said, "We gotta c'front Butler, ta main Butler. Ask him if he needs our help, if there's anythin' he thinks we uns can do ta protect our homes. We gotta let him know we're b'hind him, and maybe he'll have ideas far us. Might as well 'cept him as a neighbor, since we's all fightin' ta same battle!"

During that moment, I was proud of old Pete, impressed with his insight. A lesser man would have stuck to his old impressions of the city folks, no matter how he might witness them struggling. Still, unfortunately old Pete joined the others in doubting Will's sanity, yet he was revealing enough thoughtfulness that, for the first time, I found myself not only agreeing with him but also feeling a slight kinship with him. And I felt he would eventually think more appropriately of Will. But, after taking another breath, old Pete began rehashing the broken door incident, not sparing his colorful tongue, and I once again felt very detached from his attitude.

My clan and I were itchy to escape Hahatonka for a day, so one Sunday we all jumped into our 6-speed International and took off, eastward. We must have traveled twenty miles, reaching a town called Lake Ozark, when we saw a huge construction site.

It was the power dam being built—men swinging sledgehammers, cement pouring into man-made gullies, arches rising to support an eventual road atop the dam. How we wished we hadn't traveled that particular road. A cliff we would have imagined being a safeguard against harm and threats, a seat of its own, special, high power from which could be viewed a large part of these hills, was becoming a mere cornerstone for that power company's dam. We headed back toward Hahatonka.

Driving back, I couldn't help but contemplate Hahatonka's uncertain future, its being seized by those ruthless businessmen, and I wondered why no one except the Butlers was being approached, forewarned, about probable effects of that dam. My mind was so distraught that I couldn't make the least sense of the situation, so I began small talk with Annie so that something other than that terrible gloom would fill the air.

* * *

The week before Christmas, I made a trip to Lebanon. With little money I managed to buy each member of my clan a decent present; Annie made all her gifts, and our young ones mustered their own small tokens of the holiday meaning. Yet not even Christmas could erase the gloom, could prevent it from spreading like a plague through these hills.

One never would have guessed that folks were purchasing Christmas gifts, while they fumbled around the store, as their faces looked set for any other occasion except a gay one. Christmas had failed to bring its usual freedom from worries and lightness to spirit. But we pretended to celebrate, went through the motions, only to realize, later, that gaiety of spirit could not be feigned.

Joe and his brother must have joined their clans for Christmas day only, as a couple days before New Year's Joe walked into the store.

His quiet yet definite manner prefacing his precise words, he uttered, after taking off his hat, "Greetings, Mr. and Mrs. Amos, and happy holidays!"

Gazing out a window, he continued, "For a moment, the snow deceived me into thinking that no harm could possibly come to us here. The hills looked so safe and guarded, so calm and untouched, that I actually thought all was well—for a moment. Reality set in when I entered your store and saw no other customers. Is business as poor as it appears, at this time of year?"

I responded, "Yes, Joe, I'm afraid it is, and worse than it probably seems. It's been declining since those treecutters arrived; seems folks don't even like traveling this way; probably they're going out of their way to shop in Decaturville, and I can't rightly blame them. I'm sorry to say that my attitude is going downhill alongside the store's business."

"I imagine it is difficult being optimistic while your business is failing, but we are doing all we can to defend our rights and our land. Try keeping a stiff upper lip, Mr. Amos; I'll keep you informed."

After hearing directly from Joe, I knew all the rumors were

true, for a change, and flashes of that horrible construction site appeared before my eyes. I turned to Annie, who was going outdoors, headed, no doubt, toward her favorite thinking and dreaming spot. I didn't follow but rather started cleaning the store. Still those flashes were appearing.

On New Year's Day old Bossy returned with a calf, so I took them both to a private pen that I had finally built aside the regular pen. They seemed contented, and I considered their return a good omen. Grasping for reasons to smile, I stood watching the calf and mother's gentle, caring ways. It helped.

Rarely was school called off because of snow, but that January snow was so high, in places, that young ones would have been walking, waist high, in it, so several school days were canceled. That didn't mean that our young ones, including the smallest, were without any textbook influence, for the schoolmaster was still boarding with us, Annie and I appreciating that far more than did our young ones.

It was one of those very snowy days that Joe rushed into the store, asked if I would keep a watch over things, and explained that he was going to take his brother to the hospital. That evening there was a knock on the store door. It was Joe, again.

"Hello, Mr. Amos; did anything out of the ordinary occur during my absence?"

"No, Joe, even the treecutters took a rest today. The snow has overpowered even them! How's your brother? We've been concerned about him."

"As you probably know, his health has declined in the midst of the challenge we've been facing. I think he needs a rest, and the hospital is the best place for him. He'll be thoroughly examined, and I'm to bring him home day after tomorrow. Thank you for keeping watch. I must get some sleep now. Good evening, Mr. Amos."

That poor man, he looked worn, too. And it seemed that the bulk of estate responsibility was gradually falling on his shoulders. As I went upstairs, I heard that beautiful voice singing some opera piece, and I felt a slight relief knowing that

Joe had a release, an outlet for his worries. I comforted myself further by imagining that he felt worlds better after singing.

Those winter days passed so very slowly, giving anxiety plenty time to grow into pure fear, before any encouraging steps toward progression could be seen. By the time spring arrived, Joe had worn a path on the road around Hahatonka proper, as his brother seldom left the castle. At least, spring brought warmer weather and a fresher face to these tired-looking hills, a change that I had not looked forward to until that year.

Will left school early that year and managed to get a ride to Hahatonka. He walked into the store in his changed manner, having noticeably aged, again.

"Boy, it's good to be in these here parts, again, Ely! I missed you and your clan, these hills, and all the chances here to better my nature. Looks like no answer yet about stoppin' that power outfit, and my pa's still awful ill. How ya been?"

"Not so good, frankly, Will. Daily I become more worried about what's going to happen to these hills, and it's been a difficult winter. Did you know that construction of the dam has begun? Annie, our young ones, and I saw it this winter. Gruesome sight. But how did you do in school this past year?"

"Did better in English; all the other marks were A's again. Ya know, this was my last year of high school, so I'll be goin' back to Kansas City for graduation in a month or so. Looks like business is slippin', Ely. Stock doesn't look much different than it did when I left."

"Son, the future doesn't look good here. We're having a difficult time making ends meet. Lately I've been making only two or three trips to Lebanon a month, and those are made mostly to trade eggs and chickens for bare necessities. The greatest part of our income is from my deals with the St. Louis businessman."

"Well, Ely, it could pick up, still. We can't lose all hope of better days. If Mr. Hatch can lose his wife and still hold a clan of ten children together plus keep being such a good foreman, we should be able to hold together and stop that power company from gaining control of these waters! Every time I'm about to give up hope, I think of Mr. Hatch's strength. That always gives me a boost. You know what I mean, Ely?"

"Yes, son, but what's facing us is different than death. . . . It's not a fact of life that folks' land be ruined, crops destroyed, homes flooded—all because some group of folks decided our waters would be a good home for a big power dam. It's very difficult knowing just how to go about coping with such a threat. Electricity! There's enough here for us folks. Why can't a big source be put near Kansas City or St. Louis where large populations are? Doesn't seem at all fair that we must suffer for the sake of city folks!"

"I agree, Ely, but my pa and Uncle Joe both say life often makes us fight for what we want and what we have is not always ours to keep. In other words, we simply fight or we don't fight. I still have that old taste for candy bars and pop. Glad you've kept up the supply."

At that moment, old Pete walked in with that young helper of Mr. Hatch's. The young man speechlessly stared at Will, whose gawky frame was slouching on a counter, while old Pete, who must have been set afired to his regular ways by springtime air, or something else, tore into Will with a nasty remark.

"Hey, boy, ain't ya goin' do nothin' powerful 'bout our problems? Ya always seem ta have ta answers, eve though ya talk like us hills folks. Huh, boy, huh."

I came as close to taking a swing at Pete as that woodcutter once did. Then, such spite, plain malice, made me think old Pete was ailing in some way, and Will didn't even respond. He sat there, on the counter, looking at the ceiling as if he were oblivious to everything but his own daydreams. The young helper continued gawking at Will, while old Pete stamped the floor a couple times. I went about my work, hoping that Pete wouldn't try to involve me in some nonsensical conversation.

Vegetable planting time came, and I spent two days hoeing, planning a sizable crop. Working with the soil served as unexpected therapy, and I hoed more than was necessary. The second day some of those treecutters strolled up the road and marched across the end of my garden plot. Thinking they'd pulled a fast one, they faked an apology, having no idea what they'd done didn't phase me since they happened to stamp the area I wasn't planning to use. I continued planting, hearing their ill-meant laughter fade into the distance.

Joe's wife and two young ones returned to Hahatonka early, too. I saw them all, including a studious, pedantic looking elderly lady, get out of their car, and that solved my puzzlement concerning how the two little girls could afford to miss so much school. They all waved to me, neighborly, making me feel they were an actual part of our little community. And I was grateful for their presence.

The next day Will's older brothers drove their car up to the gas tank, pumped gas into their Model T, and took off. I guess my request completely left their minds, as did their consent to advise me whenever they took gas. So I decided it was as good a time as ever to begin marking the price of ten gallons of gas on Mr. Butler's running bill every time I saw his two eldests pumping gas. Somehow, though, it was consoling to realize that there were folks who, that there existed such folks in Hahatonka who, possessed unalterable traits.

Not more than a week after Joe's wife arrived, she strutted into the store.

"Now, Mr. Amos! Those horses and dogs make entirely too much noise, racing by here in the mornings! Will you PLEASE do something about them?"

Figuring I'd best get to a definitive answer before one of our tempers boiled over, I replied, "Madame, the horses you're referring to belong to your clan's estate, and the dogs—well, I have no idea where they come from. I'm afraid you have brought your complaint to the wrong person."

"Very well, Mr. Amos; sorry to have taken your time."

As she finished saying her piece, we both noticed our young ones all playing, hers in frilly dresses, mine in overalls, in front of the log house. It was hard to tell what they had done to get so dirty, as all we saw them doing was jumping rope, but their clothes were muddy and their skins far from their natural colors. Joe's wife had a fit, or, something close to it!

"See there, Mr. Amos. Your children are turning my daughters into roughnecks. I must forbid yours to play with mine. You do understand, DON'T you?"

Doing all I could, once again, to hold back the laughter, I merely nodded and pretended to look over the garden while she ran across the road and dragged her young ones inside their house. My young ones looked to me, and I motioned them into the store, not feeling the least compelled to reprimand them for anything. I'd hoped even Joe's wife could learn to accept certain ways in these hills, but I instantly realized that I was expecting too much of her.

The tomatoes surely did grow well that year, so I gave a big bag of them to each nearby clan—the Hatches, Joe's clan, and the folks who lived between us and the old schoolhouse. I set some on the steps of the white house, another of the buildings especially built to home castle workers, because whatever hired helpers stayed in there could have used the tomatoes, too. And, shortly after I placed those tomatoes, that young helper of Mr. Hatch's stepped outside to fetch them.

Though the white house stood only about fifty feet from the log house, I'd never paid much attention to who went in and out; but I should have guessed that young helper was staying there, because he was practically always in sight, somewhere on our hill when he wasn't in the boat. His primary job on the estate was to give river tours, but eight times out of ten, I would guess, Joe's wife was the one being paddled down the river. Seems those two enjoyed each other's company, or, perhaps Joe's wife enjoyed boating.

Speaking of tours, River Cave entertained the largest share of tourists. Near its opening, there was a hill from where a natural spring began, visibly in a strong rainfall. And that spring went through the cave, under it in places, under a sizable part of Hahatonka, and showed itself again at the Big Spring. Tours through the cave continued day in and day out; while other businesses began slowing, River Cave still hosted an almost continuous line of tourists. The helpers who worked that cave didn't know many idle moments, and they had to be knowledgeable about attractions inside that cave.

Lilacs and hundreds other flowers were showing their faces in these hills, and every tree was showing a sign of new life. Then overnight, it seemed, summer's heat came to remind us of past years when our worst problem was keeping cool. That is, the heat augmented every sound of change, somehow made it pierce our ears and souls harder and made it stay with us longer. There was no getting away from the torment.

Mouth of River Cave

LARGEST STALAGMITE IN THE WORLD, RIVER CAVE, HA HA TONKA, MO.

However, as I mentioned, there were certain traits that remained changeless—among those was the log house clan's obsession with partying. But their dancing on the road and carrying on until wee hours was not the maddening distraction it once had been. Matter of fact, some local folks were beginning to join the festivities, young and old alike, and the parties seemed much more civilized. I was even growing accustomed to falling asleep to Ragtime.

* * *

The first inevitable discussion about condemnation notices from the power company finally happened, one sultry July day, as the threatening gloom was, in a very true sense, visibly hanging over these hills. That old potbellied stove was spit on and kicked, unjustly, as tempers and emotions flared.

"Fellows, we uns in far some fightin' whether we wanta or not! Some goddarn lawyer brung me a paper sayin' OUR property it's goin' be under water a year from now! I shut ta door in his goddarn face!"

In walked Joe to check on his mail, and the talk stopped. He nodded to the group, thanked me for the mail, and left as quietly as he'd entered. I noticed a bitter sigh when he spotted a particular letter, business, from the power company, and I considered withholding that letter, knowing myself that it would be bad news; but, good as it was, my intention would have produced only a temporary relief and an illegal act so I handed him the whole lot.

As soon as Joe left, the group continued, and Pete himself was emotionally triggered at having received a notice, too.

"My life's wrapped in my farm, only place I know ta live. My ma had me there and my wife had all our kids there, and I worked ever inch a ta soil there with my own hands. I wouldn't know how ta make it elsewheres. Ain't never thought a another home."

Poor old Pete brought us all to the edge of tears. Just then, Will walked in.

"Howdy, Ely; gentlemen. Ely, look here what I found at the bottom of the cliff under the castle. More artifacts!"

Pete's group all snickered but didn't phase Will's enthusiasm, as Will continued, "Those Indians knew how to fight, protect, and hold on to what they wanted. History tells us that in 1806 the Osages were ordered out of these hills by the President of the United States, but they didn't give up for almost twenty years!"

Then Will hopped on top the counter, sat down, and spoke on. This is what he said:

> No, those Indians fought! They knew these hills were theirs. Hahatonka was theirs! Though its fate didn't include them, still they returned to visit their true home. Hahatonka took in different inhabitants, but that didn't change the Osages' feeling and attachment. We might say they ultimately lost the battle—but they survived—still, that this was THEIR home!
>
> We've got to know that Hahatonka is our home—then we'll never have to surrender!

Certainly the snickering had stopped and full attention was given Will's words, but old Pete broke the silence by feebly attempting a response.

"Well, boy, ya aa a said a mouthful. We heared ya but we's shocked ya can talk like that. Give us uns time ta think. Ya ain't been in these parts half as long as us so don't think ya tellin' us anythin' new. Sides, injuns didn't mind where they hunted and fished and made those arraheads. They could do that anywheres. How ya know they FELT a special way 'bout this land? Huh, boy?"

Will shook his head, almost ashamedly, probably for Pete, jumped off the counter, and asked me if he could help himself to some candy bars. And I figured any response on my part would only prompt Pete and his group to further their ignorant talk, so I just nodded to Will. He left with his pockets full of candy bars and a soda in each hand.

"Now, what us locals gonna do 'bout them damned notices we's a gettin'?"

"That 'tarded boy didn't sound so 'tarded juss then. Pete, ya maybe shouldn't a talked like ya did ta him. He don't seem such a bad boy."

"Don't go on 'bout some crazy boy. We's got business to decuss. I think us uns oughta teer up ever notice we get and claim we ain't never saw such paper!"

"Na, that would't work. Them papers a dime a dozen. Power company juss keep givin' em ta us till we'd quit terin' em up. Best we come up with some tactics."

I don't think anything but sheer bitterness was expressed in that day's bull session. It continued for hours, and Annie wouldn't come downstairs so I had to succumb to that ridiculous talk while I handled the mail and served what few customers could stand it long enough to place their orders. Twice that afternoon I suggested to Pete and his group that they go home and think it all out, but they insisted their gathering was most important to reaching a decision, a "tactic."

The hot days rolled on and these hills were looking a little scorched. And Will kept so busy that his visits dwindled to minutes each, always before or after some duty or mission. It was hard to tell just what his overall plan was, but something surely was motivating him to keep watch over various power company activities. In the heat of an afternoon, Will could be seen walking about these hills, or up and down the road, walking as if his feet couldn't move quickly enough.

As summer ended, more notices were issued; still folks didn't know what to do. It seemed no one could believe his home would eventually be under a big lake or that these hills would ever be overcome by water. So the notices to vacate didn't take on their intended effect; they only antagonized folks into any uproar and caused added tension within Pete's group's gatherings.

I began looking forward to hearing Joe's singing in the evenings. Almost nightly, after sundown, he'd stroll to some nearby hill, hardly ever sang on our hill, and bellow at least two songs. Will had told me that his uncle was a musician at heart and that he probably would have pursued a full-time singing career had not so much family business fallen into his lap. He surely had a beautiful voice, and, as time went by, he followed each opera piece with a regular song, probably for the sake of us locals. Many an evening our small community of tormented minds and souls was soothed by Joe's sweet singing.

* * *

Stopping for candy bars during one of his missions, Will was talking faster than I imagined he possibly could, actually faster than I'd heard any human being talk.

"Ely, all the folks 'cept me and Uncle Joe are leavin' today. It'll be good for my father to be in a different place for a while, and I'll like havin' the house to myself. Bet you didn't even realize when I went to Kansas City for graduation. Goin' to take a break from school, this year; then I'll go to college. Where's Annie? I got a taste of one of her last cakes, and it was mighty good; wanted to tell her. Oh, well, I'll tell her later. Gotta go. See ya, Ely."

Off he went before I could answer.

Chapter VII

PRIOR TO 1931

As if Pete's group didn't have enough rattling their minds, no sooner than the Butlers left, there was a bull session solely dedicated to the ghost matter, the spirits that had returned to the castle. It was one late September day, when the gloom was heavier than ever, that those minds gathered to trigger each other's imagination, very successfully.

"Here we is, s'rounded by them ghosts 'gain. I saw em, three or four, circlin' 'round ta castle. Hear tell ta 'tarded boy's only one there now. Guess he and ta spooks get 'long all right."

"Maybe he don't know he's bein' visited by ghosts. Maybe somebody oughta tell him. He might be in danger there all 'lone."

"Don't worry none 'bout that boy. Ghosts'd probably run from him!"

Just then Mrs. Ida Maines came in to give her usual weather report, almost always the same report as any other time, and to check on her mail. Exactly as I feared, she overheard Pete's group and hollered at the top of her lungs. That instantly silenced the group, but, after calming down, she insisted on hearing more about the ghosts, so old Pete readily obliged her.

"Well, Mrs. Maines, we uns here has been seein' critters, spooky lookin' things, swarmin' ta castle when there ain't no Butlers there, but now that 'tarded boy's still there and ta ghosts a visitin' anyways. We's 'fraid they'll scatter into ta hills and next thin' be visitin' our homes. That there's what all ta c'motion's 'bout.

Mrs. Maines didn't respond immediately, just stood there looking scared, then finally thanked Peter for the information

THE CASTLE HAHATONKA MO
151

and assured the gentlemen she'd spread the word. And, that, I knew she would.

Pete and his group conjured more ghosts and plotted further means of controlling them, yet, ghosts or no ghosts, a solution to our more urgent problem was being ignored. It seemed that only the Butlers were facing reality and coping with the gloom that was gradually, wherever not quickly, touching all our lives. The store standing on such a high hill, it was not in danger of being flooded, but it might as well have been doomed to that exact fate as business suffered all the effects of Hahatonka's growing anxiety. Ironic how, without it being talked about, folks were showing their fear and resentment.

Seldom as it was, I still traveled to Lebanon, mostly to trade since cash was becoming more scarce. One day I was no farther on the road than between River Cave and the Red Sink when I spotted Will racing through the canyon. He'd become adept at riding a horse, and he masterfully brought the animal to a halt. I couldn't help but be curious about what he was doing out there, since he'd been spending so little time in leisure, so I pulled the 6-speed International over and jumped out to have a look.

Will was meeting his uncle Joe, who was reading something, in the middle of the Red Sink. They sat together, both of them appearing to be holding the weight of the world on their shoulders. I just got in the truck and took off, drove as fast as I could, hoping to leave behind some of that terrible gloom.

When I returned that evening, Will was in the store and was plenty upset about something.

"I'm glad to see ya, Ely. Things are looking mighty poor. That power company has condemned the old grist mill, says it'll be under water by next fall. But Uncle Joe says we'll keep it runnin', like everything else, until all hope is gone. Between you and me, Ely, Hahatonka's future doesn't look too promising. Still I want to keep some faith that we can hold our own against some power company. And our law suit's goin' to court this winter."

As Will paused, Joe's voice could be heard, that remarkable

singing, and we listened with all our hearts. He was singing some old ballad, and it brought tears to Will's eyes. If I had been a crying sort, I would have shed some tears just then, too; instead I sat on the stairs, put my head between my legs, and tried to be carried away by Joe's music, to the country mentioned in the song.

That night neither Annie nor I could sleep, so we told our eldest to watch the other two while we took a walk. We went to the natural bridge, which was still our special spot, and watched the stars. That helped relax us, but we both knew our anxieties were justified. At least, for Annie and me, the natural bridge still held a certain charm that set us to romantic ways. A little more ready for sleep, we mosied back home.

If we had had roosters still, they would have been crowing at the same time when someone was banging on the store door that next morning. I looked out an upstairs window to see a gang of woodcutters as drunk as folks could be. Momentarily considering not answering so that they'd have to contend with Joe's wife's sure reprimand, my better senses told me they'd probably break down the door if I didn't see what they wanted so I put on some pants and went downstairs.

"Oil, ye old hillbilly; we're 'bout outa lamp oil and we'll need it in ta places we're workin' today. Open up!"

Thinking I was making a mistake but not knowing what else to do, I opened the door, just in time to be pushed against the counter. That stirred my temper, and I ordered them to take what they wanted and I'd add it on their monthly bill, reminding them of their considerable debt. They more or less ignored what I said, fumbled around like uncontrollable animals, broke a couple oil lamps, grabbed a jar of candy and several cans of oil, then stumbled away, as loudly as they'd entered. While I was trying to itemize their bill, I noticed a light flickering in the log house. Whoever was behind that lamp saw and heard those darn woodcutters, and I belligerently hoped it was Joe's wife so that the woodcutters wouldn't have heard the last of that incident.

The restaurant was condemned, the same time as the grist

mill, and that gave those woodcutters all the approval they needed to use the building as an outlet for their terrorist ways. Windows were broken, walls used as carving boards, and items within either removed or destroyed. No action was taken against the woodcutters since the management, who leased the building from the Butlers, had deserted after receiving the condemnation notice. Probably they were tired of struggling and saw the notice as a valid excuse to give up and move on. And since the restaurant building was least of the estate concerns, the woodcutters triumphed, scott-free of any due punishment.

Without the restaurant's returning patronage to look forward to, the store's future looked even dimmer. Seeing the empty, defaced building, that once sheltered an almost constant bustle of tourists, was just another depressing reminder of the tragedy approaching these hills and put a harshly pathetic slant to walks along the spring path.

Business was usually good until Thanksgiving, but that year it sank to an all-time low by October and dampened our spirits further. Locals' trade had never been enough to support the store, and that October it seemed tourists were coming only as far as Hahatonka's edge, just to take a glance of its original beauty and to tour River Cave, then were leaving to avoid being touched by the spreading plunder and spoilage.

A couple days after the woodcutters' onslaught, Will looked every bit as angry as he said he was when he walked into the store.

"There's no justice in these hills! Ely, what are we goin' do? A building is demolished and no one does a darn thing 'bout it! My blood's boilin! My pa's sicker by the day, and this news won't help, and my uncle Joe's got his hands so full I'm afraid he can't hold up much longer. Who's goin' watch out for those outlaws, the ones that are campin' on this land?

Did you ever read or hear about the Slicker War, Ely? Well, it happened right here. Settlers were tryin' to make their homes here, farm the land, and so on, while outlaws of all kinds were operatin', stealin', threatenin', and doin' everything else they could to make the settlers move on. There was fightin', awful fightin'. What few settlers there were all joined forces to protect themselves; they learned to punish the bandits that stole from them. They were brave folks, those settlers, and finally they overcame—after losin' a lot and after fightin' darn hard!"

Finally I was able to contribute a word or so, edgewise, "Yes, I know about the Slicker War. It was a mess."

"Well, Ely, I think we're relivin' it or startin' a new war, what few of us care. But we need means of punishin' the attackers, rather preventin' them from doing as they please 'round here. That law suit fights 'gainst the power company, but it doesn't stop the day-to-day attacks. Fact is, it doesn't seem to be stoppin' the power company much either. Hear tell more folks been gettin' condemnation notices. Wish Mr. Hinley and his gang could do something besides bullshit! They appear so full of spunk yet they seem scared to do anything serious."

"I know what you mean, Will. They're quite a gang. I'm afraid we can't expect too much courage or forethought from them. They have never had to face such things as those surrounding us now."

Hearing a gallop that caused us both to stop and look outside, we saw Mr. Hatch ride to the barn beside his house, change horses, and take off again. Seems he was doing everything in fast motion, those days, and Will noticed it, too.

"He keeps more horses in that barn than in the stone barn, here lately. He's always on the go; guess it's more convenient for him to take off from home than from across the way. That man's teachin' me an awful lot, Ely. He's not much for talkin', mostly doin' things, keepin' busy. I'd best be gettin' busy myself. I'm goin' keep an eye on those wicked woodcutters, for a while. If I see them doin' anything unlawful, I'm goin' hop on a horse and get the law and bring them out here!"

While Will ran out, his older brothers drove up in one of their cars, filled it with gas, and took off. I marked ten gallons worth on their father's bill and returned to my duties.

One of those autumn days, when I was certain these hills were the most beautiful, blessed place on earth, Annie calmly explained to me that our young ones had been missing since noon. It was almost four o'clock, so I ran out and called for them, several times. After a few minutes, we panicked. With all the recently strange occurrences coming to mind, I took off, on foot, toward the natural bridge. As I screamed, the only response was an echo of my own voice, but I continued screaming. Finally I returned home to get the truck and found Annie contending with a group of those nasty treecutters. I ordered them away, but they laughed and sneered. I picked up a shotgun and pointed it at them, and that made them scatter. Then I closed the store, early, so that Annie and I both could look for our young ones. And I took that shotgun with me.

We didn't think of driving up the castle road, but we should have. We met our young ones being led across the natural bridge by Will.

"Look here, Annie and Ely! Look who I found up at the greenhouses! They've been gettin' a breath of fresh air, according to your daughter. The baby acts hungry."

I didn't know whether I should laugh or, for the first time in years, cry, while Annie did enough crying for the both of us. But certainly I questioned our eldest, and she gave me a likely answer.

"Pa, we need some breath of fresh Ozark air. The Butler girls need it, they say, and we decided we need it, too. The greenhouses, lookin' so pretty on the cliff, was the perfect place. The time flew, and we're so sorry we worried you and ma."

After hearing her reasoning, I could hardly keep a straight face, not to mention reprimand her, so I mustered the best lecture I could under the circumstances. I guess it was effective as Annie and I never again faced that particular scare.

These hills were shining their brightest that autumn, almost any color sparkling somewhere within them, and there was no disguise in that blessing. When all seemed hopeless, I looked to these hills and they not only eased my fears but also somehow belittled that constant gloom. Nothing could have been more overpowering, more exalted, than these hills, from where I stood; I was certain, as I put all my concerns in their arms and, each time, gained a new confidence.

According to old Pete and his group, the castle ghosts had multiplied and were haunting the natural bridge area as well as traveling the road to the castle. Being the lead alarmist, Pete organized control measures, since the ghosts had enlarged their army, so all concerned locals either respectively stood their night posts or searched for tracks, evidence, so on, during the day. They were a busy crew, and, by Thanksgiving time, they were sure ghost activities were enough under surveillance that soon the nasty varmints would take their sport elsewhere. And that was a relief to us all.

* * *

Just after Thanksgiving, Will's father returned to Hahatonka, probably to prepare for the upcoming trial. I knew about the trial the day after Thanksgiving—when an attorney subpoenaed me to serve as witness in the lawsuit of Hahatonka Estate verses that electric and power company.

Several other local folks and I were supposed to verify that high water marks were indeed being placed in sufficient advance of the actual flooding, and it seemed most unfair that we had to support Hahatonka invaders. I was sorely dreading the moment when I would have to testify that the methods being used to flood Hahatonka were just, and I've never been involved in a greater or more distressing irony than that of swearing to a proper plan to deface these hills.

The horrible ordeal came and went much faster, though more painfully, than I had imagined. Having fulfilled our peculiar duties, a few days before Christmas we witnesses were returned home, and I endured that next week without feeling a trace of holiday spirit.

Then, one by one and clan by clan, local folks filed into the log house on New Year's Eve, as an open invitation had been spread about these hills. For that one evening, the log house seemed as much a part of these hills as the trees and cliffs themselves, and even I momentarily escaped what woes and threats were crowding my life and almost tasted the holiday spirit. But the crowd's gaiety and merrymaking didn't shake Will's changed nature, in fact, didn't seem to lighten his spirits, at all. He spoke to me on his way home.

"Ely, I feel guilty being here. I'm spoiling folks' good times, and my pa might need me at home. Ma deserves this evening out amongst folks, so, since my brothers are in the city, I'd better check on my pa. His health is growing worse, and he needs all the support I can give him. Hope you enjoy the rest of the party. Happy New Year, Ely."

As Will found his way onto the snow covered road, Joe's wife sat down at their piano and began playing one Christmas carol after another until finally Joe started singing. It took some prompting on his part, but eventually Joe got folks, old Pete included, to humming and singing along with him. And, as far as I could tell, it was that New Year's Eve gathering that laid seed for the growth of a brotherhood amongst Hahatonka's folks.

Chapter VIII

1931–PART 1

Court proceedings began again, so Joe and his brother left Hahatonka, Will close in their tracks, but it wasn't long before Mr. Butler was returned because of illness. Joe carried the burden in court while Mr. Butler attempted recovery, enough to rejoin the trial. But he never regained his health.

It was a very mournful, frightening day when Will's father died, and word of his death spread about these hills with the same speed of any news. By the day of the funeral, everyone who had attended the recent party was present in the store to await instructions as to where he or she might attend the funeral. It was a moving experience, for me, being a part of the emotional bond that filled the store on that sad day.

Joe and Will entered together, followed by Joe's wife and daughters. Though his voice was quivering, Joe was the only Butler not in tears, as he spoke to the crowd.

"Your presence is so much appreciated on this unhappy occasion, and the entire family earnestly welcomes each of you to attend a brief service at the natural bridge which will follow a private ceremony for the family. We sincerely thank you all for your sympathy."

After Joe and his clan and Will left, all us other folks waited in the store until we saw two black limousines and a black hearse slowly drive down the castle road. Then we all walked to the natural bridge and stood before the hearse. All the Butlers, except Will's mother, stepped out of their limousines, and a man of the cloth briefly spoke about the inevitable end to each person's earthly life and about the ultimate end to all things as we know them. Then the Butlers re-entered the limousines and headed for Kansas City, where Mr. Butler was to be buried, and we local folks went our respective ways.

Not much fairness or justice surrounded our lives, those days, and that terrible gloom was growing more and more visible. Though the winter months brought us a temporary sense of safety by turning the waters into ice, making us think these hills were untouchable, soon spring time came to show us that little was sacred. The rising Niangua was forcing Hahatonka Lake to spew into Big Spring so that it crept closer to the spring path, week by week. Bearing its already weathered condemnation sign, the old mill was reopened to once again serve farmers' needs, but a vast, green field no longer bordered its frame. And, no longer having the spacious mill grounds to host Saturday get togethers, folks waited in their wagons, or trucks, until there was room enough near the mill to stand in line.

Will was playing an active part in seeing that the old mill continue its function; hardly a Saturday passed that he wasn't assisting the mill operator. Matter of fact, Will was becoming Mr. Hatch's right-hand man, overseeing many jobs that kept the estate in reasonable order. Fortunately those darn treecutters had moved their campsite (exactly where, remained a mystery), so the mill operation and the crawfish trapping had rising waters as their worst enemy. And Will saw to it that both businesses, on either side of the island, ran efficiently.

Will was becoming more a man each time I saw him, which was less and less while his responsibilities increased. He had so little idle time, while his brothers seemed to have nothing but time on their hands, and unfortunately I was seeing more of them than of Will. Frankly I didn't know why they didn't stay in the city instead of coming to these hills and complaining about being here. Will was the only son, as far as I could tell, who showed signs of having lost a father, unless his older brothers' signs were in the form of expandingly wild ways.

During one of the rare moments, that spring, when Will had more than five minutes to chat with me, Gus and Carl wheeled right up to the gas tank, missing it by about two inches. As we watched them gas their Model-T, Will spoke, randomly, of inner changes he was feeling.

"Huh, my brothers and I practically ignore each other; we're in different worlds. Until recently I looked up to them, respected them, for some of their cleverness. Now I can't think of any way that they impress me. Since my pa died, I've been talking a lot to ma and we're getting closer to each other's meanings, each other's core. I think she's a very special person, and she tells me I'm most like pa was and even more like my grandpa. Says, though I wasn't even born before he died, I must have known him in spirit, somehow. Maybe I'm finding out what she means by that."

Admittedly I wasn't too sure what exactly Will was saying, but I did realize he was growing into a man. Everything about him betrayed any trace of a teenage boy, almost uncanny how he was changing, so quickly, so gracefully. We talked on.

"Will, how's your mother doing? She hasn't ordered cakes for quite a while."

"Ma has remarkable strength. She keeps telling me we're all mortals and if we accept that fact, it helps us make the most of life and accept its ending. Ma lives in a deep sadness, though, without pa, like part of her own self has died. They were so close to each other, but Ma's known other tragedies and says she realizes living is not a completely happy experience. Her world is a realistic one, and it's a stronghold for me. She's an amazing person; she'll be all right. I'll tell her you asked about her. But don't expect her to be ordering cakes, at least, for a while. I doubt if she'll be hosting any parties in the near future."

With that, Will moised out the door, and I stood looking over half stocked shelves and bare counters. There was no doubt in my mind that Annie and I had to grip our predicament, our failing business. So I went upstairs to bring the matter out in the open.

Annie led me to her dream spot, across the road, just inside the woods. There we gazed at the castle, standing so awesomely and lonely atop all of Hahatonka. For a brief moment, I entered Annie's state, that that particular spot encouraged, and saw why

Annie found her relief there. But I knew the sensation couldn't hold us for long, so I ended the bliss by suggesting that we sell all our merchandise and find someone else to take over Annie's postal duties. And I was amazed at her clearsighted approach to what was surrounding us.

"Dear, I've known for quite some time that our future's welfare will depend on how soon we can leave Hahatonka. Last time you were in Lebanon, a businessman from the city, I've forgot just what city, was here. When he mentioned his field was buying and selling, I asked if he might be interested in our store business. He wasn't, but someone will be. We'll just keep trying until we're given an offer, any offer. If we lose much more, I feel we should go away, even if we can't sell our stock or find another postmaster. Surely the Butlers would understand. Since Mr. Butler's no longer with us, I guess we should send the estate's bill, minus our rent, to Will's mother. Or should we send it to Joe?"

I didn't know how to answer that, as I didn't know how to respond to any of what she'd just said. Annie's sense of reality was astonishing; I hadn't given her enough credit for that, but then neither of us had ever faced such a horrible situation before. We were seeing new aspects of each other, and I felt as if most of what I had been sure of was changing and I wasn't attuned to any of it. Annie continued talking.

"I've been asking folks if they've seen anything of those tree-cutters. It's as if they have disappeared, and I guess you know that we haven't received payment for that large supply of axes. It's bad enough that we've sunk to accepting farmers' goods instead of cash, but we haven't received anything from those woodcutters. I don't know where we can send their bill. . . ."

I held Annie in my arms, not knowing any other way to react, any appropriate words. We sat there until the castle became a silhouette in the sky.

* * *

A tourist had once told me that some of the creatures, cranes and ducks, on Hahatonka Lake reminded him of water nymphs he'd seen in fairytale books. Since the day I learned of water nymphs, I began wondering if Joe's wife thought she was one. I've never seen anyone spend so much time in a boat, almost unnatural, for pure riding, never fishing or paddling herself. Though river tours was never the most successful endeavor in Hahatonka, still that young helper of Mr. Hatch's was kept plenty busy.

When I dared to mention his aunt's obvious fondness of the waters, Will merely said she was never the domestic, indoor sort. Then, sharing another observation with Will brought me equal reprimand. I mentioned that his aunt seemed so jovial with Mr. Hatch's young helper, and Will said his aunt always wanted a son.

As Will had little time for small talk, he had less time for nonsense, and he put me in my place more than once when I strayed from matters at hand.

It was a beautiful, sunny May day, when the weather itself almost lightened that thick gloom, that Will told me of the lawsuit's regression.

"Ely, things are looking worse. Our attorneys are good, and they're doing their best, but the power company holds the favorable opinion—that they'd be improving on our land by making our waters connect to a big lake. The defense has a powerful case—that Hahatonka's beauty would be enhanced, not partly covered, and more accessible by boat if it connected to higher waters. The jurors would have to know these hills as you and I do in order to take our side, to see the reason for the lawsuit. But, then, beauty is something different in different folks' eyes."

As eager as I was to hear Will's report, I wished it hadn't ruined a dream that the May day had allowed to slip into my mind, a dream that everyone in the courtroom would be touched, somehow, by Hahatonka's eminence and glory and would be compelled to uphold its rights to be left alone, untouched. Everywhere my mind turned reality was there to meet it, and Will was becoming a major catalyst of that reality.

* * *

Old Pete and his group spent an entire spring day in the store. Talk was cheap, requiring nothing but their imaginations' force, and certainly they were plenty inspired, constantly. That particular day their primary concern was the reason their hair were turning gray, and such reasoning could come only from the likes of those minds hovered around the old potbellied stove. This is part of what I heard.

"Pete, ya hairs turned all gray so quicklike. Never saw a man's hair do that, in one season!"

"Yep, ain't it a sight. Probably from them ghosts. I hears it's a plague they do when they can't spook folks. I knows it was gonna come ta me 'cause I comed up with a way ta chase em critters aways. It gonna happen ta some ya others, juss watch and see!"

"No ghosts gonna change my hair," that kind, elderly gentleman said as he took off his straw hat and bent over to expose his bald head, his lighthearted tone putting an end to the subject, fortunately.

Will walked in about that time, and he overlooked a puzzled group of men. They gawked at Will as if he were a stranger. He was wearing the usual overalls, no shoes, and no shirt, but his hair was cut and he looked especially well groomed. I assumed he had just stepped out of a dress suit, having returned, again, from that trial, but Pete and his group saw only a new haircut. No one made a snide remark or even mumbled under his breath; they just stared. Will greeted me, nodded to the group, took his regular share of candy bars and soda, and raced back out.

Then I heard, "That boy ain't as 'tarded as he use ta be, his pa a dyin' could a straightin' him out some. . . ." and shut my ears, finally being able to tell them it was closing time.

That evening Annie and I took inventory, then looked over our financial books. And we knew, without a doubt, that our survival in Hahatonka was ending. It was that night that Annie and I told our young ones we would be leaving soon. But their questions about where we were going and when we would be leaving couldn't be answered.

Tornado-type gales whipped around these hills late that spring, and several times I thought the log house, along with other buildings except the ones of stone, would leave the ground. The sun was bright, sky was clear, and all the sudden, one day, clouds started flying and trees started bending every direction, and I was on the road in the old 6-speed International.

That truck floated around the road until finally I reached home, just as a big oak fell across the road. I jumped out to try moving the huge log, but it wouldn't budge, so I shouted for help. And there came Joe, running to my rescue. The two of us pushed with all our might, not effecting that big oak tree. Then Mr. Hatch rode up, took a rope off his saddle, tied one end to his saddle and the other to the oak, and put that horse into action. The animal pulled that log away easier than ten men could have. Joe ran back to the log house, and I took off for the store, and Mr. Hatch rode into the distance. As I observed his riding skill, I saw another tree fall near his path—as if those woodcutters hadn't done a thorough enough job.

* * *

An entire week passed without a single customer except the folks who came for mail. As the weather calmed, a few stray travelers happened into the store, each one inquiring about Hahatonka's ghostly appearance, and one traveler asked me how that dam being constructed was going to effect folks' lives and farmers' land. I didn't have any more answers for those folks than I did for my own young ones. But that didn't prevent folks from quizzing me about everything from who lived in that castle to how folks survived in these hills.

Early June, one Sunday, Will came to me to ask if I'd drive him to the construction site. Annie didn't want to go, and I didn't give our young ones a choice, so Will and I took the drive by ourselves. Nothing would suit him but to walk right up to the dam, which was almost completed, and I went with him. It was uglier than before, all those gates waiting to be opened by men who would be hired to control the water's force. I stood there wondering if the Almighty were frowning on the cement contraption, its massive proof of man's ignorant step into civilization. Electrical power, enough to serve the whole state—at the expense of many folks' homes and livelihoods.

Will wasn't very talkative that day. As we drove back to Hahatonka, our thoughts probably met, several times, but not many words were exchanged. The waters looked higher, considerably higher, but I didn't mention that either. As we passed the River Cave drive, we both noticed that there wasn't a line of tourists waiting to enter the cave. We pulled over and saw that the platform, atop steps leading down to the cave, had been slightly destroyed, evidently by the recent gales. There weren't even any hired helpers in sight. Will finally spoke his mind.

"There haven't been any reports of this damage. I'd better tell Uncle Joe or Mr. Hatch. Or maybe we should let it be. It doesn't seem too important amidst what other concerns we're dealing with. First the restaurant, now this; next . . . Really none of those things matter. What matters is that these hills stay untouched, uncovered, left alone. That power dam is the biggest threat to Hahatonka. And I'm going back to the trial, tomorrow, to see if I can be put on the witness stand. I've plenty to say, and I'm ready to say it!"

I believed him and prayed that he could be heard and understood by everyone in the courtroom, so I wished him luck. I was dreaming a miracle, but I wished it just the same.

"Jumpin' snakes! A snake!" I heard when I walked into the store. There was Annie, trembling in a corner; above her were the three young ones all peeping, fearfully, around the stairway.

The steps had no railing, so I told them to get back and stay upstairs until I said elsewise. Then I asked Annie where it was, just when I saw a rattler coiled on the floor about six feet from Annie.

"Don't move," I whispered. Then I hurried to the truck where I kept a shotgun strapped under the seat. I loaded the gun and ran back to the store. That was the most nervous moment in my life mainly because I never had a sure aim. I caught my breath, raised that shotgun, and kept telling myself that no one could miss a big rattler at only twenty feet. I fired, missed, fired again while the snake was moving. That time I hit it and sat down before I took another breath. Annie ran to me so our bodies could quiver alongside each other.

Our young ones wouldn't come down until the dead snake was removed, and I didn't blame them. Frankly I wasn't eager to go near even a dead snake, so I picked it up with a couple strong sticks and carried it to the woods behind the store. We all thought we'd survived a dangerous experience. And I guess we had.

1931—PART 2

I was picking watercress from the spring, heard a faint scream, looked toward the lake—and, sure enough, it was Joe's wife, boating with that young helper. She'd fallen into the water, again, but seemed to be enjoying the mishap. She swam to the island, disappeared for a brief while, then reappeared near the cave opening and struck up conversation.

"Hello, Mr. Amos! Isn't this the greenest green of any waters you've ever seen? I'm growing quite attached to these waters, their colorful, peaceful sight, their inviting ways. I'm going to miss them, terribly miss them."

Not awaiting any response, she swam away, holding watercress in one hand and halfway waving with the other hand. She got around pretty well in the water, and I immediately thought about what that tourist had told me about water nymphs. She was even taking on the supposedly pleasant personality of a water nymph, but she still had the appearance of a regular woman. That lady inspired me toward thinking some crazy thoughts.

With a basket full of watercress, I started climbing the uphill path and saw Joe in the woods. He was singing something that sounded like the blues music I had once heard at a Negro gospel concert in Lebanon. They were awfully moanful, repetitive lyrics. If I could have carried a tune, I would have joined him. As it was, I paused on the hill and listened. Then Joe spotted me.

"Mr. Amos, greetings! I was trying a different kind of music that I've always admired. It suddenly came to me, naturally. . . . I'd better return to the house, so I'll walk the path with you. . . . Probably you've heard that the lawsuit isn't going our way. And I'm concerned about the effect on this community if the power company wins, that is, if water covers not only parts of Hahatonka but also most of the lowlands. Do you happen to know if local people are taking steps to combat the power company?"

Unfortunately I ashamedly had to tell Joe that local folks seemed to be avoiding the entire matter, though they were receiving condemnation notices on their homes. I attempted a reason for their peculiar ways, that it was the hillbilly's trait to hide from any changes that might come their way and to ignore any foreigners' threats. Then Joe looked as if some puzzle had just been solved.

"Ah, that explains the defense attorneys' mention of having shotguns aimed at them upon several occasions while delivering notices. Those incidents haven't helped our case, at all; they bring sympathy to the power company's cause. Mr. Amos, do you feel there's any possibility of reasoning with local people, trying to convince them of organized courses they could be taking?"

I shook my head and told Joe not to waste his time, for he might as well have thought of trying to push that cement dam with his own force rather than attempting to sway a hillbilly's stubbornness. We shook hands and went our separate ways.

"What in tarnation ya goin' do with all them lettuce?" Pete said, bracing against the doorframe as if he owned the store.

I told him what they were and just what my clan and I were going to do with them, as if it were any of his business. He chuckled, weakly.

"Time ta tend the crops," said old Pete before he kicked open the door and marched away, seemingly without a care.

Just then something struck my inner self like a bolt of lightning, or like a flash of clear light. Suddenly I wanted to attend the trial, so I told Annie I would be leaving the next morning and didn't know how long I'd be gone. I left at dawn, thinking only of asking Will to go along, but I knew he'd been staying near the courthouse for days.

I found a seat in the courtroom, just in time to hear Will make his plea to the jury. I'd no idea how he had arranged to have the floor, but it was well worth the time taken from, or added to, the trial. Words flowed from his mouth like the Big Spring water rolled over the mill dam, and not a whisper or creaky chair interrupted his entire speech. This part I remember, verbatim:

> Yes, land is land, and there's much of it in this country, much beautiful land. But Hahatonka is my home, every inch of it, and I beg you to realize that my hills, and the waters as they are, are there for you, too; their beauty, splendor, and glory is closeby everyone who sits in this courtroom. And how rare is such varied beauty found in one setting! If the waters are rearranged around Hahatonka and raised to cover parts of it, it will still be my home! The hills of Hahatonka will not have changed in my eyes and soul and mind—but they will have lost something in the naked eye; eyes that have yet to behold them will see them robbed of their full splendor. It is those who have not yet seen Hahatonka, who have yet to walk the spring path, that I ask you to consider. . . .

His speech was much longer; he talked about the importance of the old mill and the necessity of the Big Spring's pure water for trout, as he spoke for all the local folks. After he finished, I left the courtroom, to collect myself, and returned in time to hear the judge.

"Will the Butler heirs please rise."

Will stood, alone. He apologized for the absence of the other family members and offered to represent them as spokesman. The judge looked to Will and Hahatonka's attorneys and proceeded.

"Beauty is something difficult to adjudge or to measure. . . . Now the jury will face their difficult task. . . ."

Will and I returned to Hahatonka, together, and he went into the store for some candy bars and soda. Waiting there were

Annie, with a big smile on her face, and a stranger, well dressed and serious looking. Will started eating candy bars, and Annie introduced me to the stranger.

"Ely, this gentleman is offering us one thousand dollars for the store merchandise. What do you think?"

I said to Annie, "Let's not think it over!" then turned to the businessman and said, "We accept your offer!"

The next day, with Will's able assistance, my clan and I were packing our belongings and loading the old 6-speed International. Will rode with us as far as the natural bridge, where he hopped out.

"Hope you settle somewhere in these hills!" he said as he stood on the road to his house and smiled as only the heir to these hills could have smiled.

EPILOGUE

We traveled eastward until we reached an intersection of two roads. There stood more buildings than we'd seen in one location, for a long time, and beyond them was bare ground, as far as the eye could see. We saw a post office, pulled up to it and went inside to ask if there might be an empty house nearby.

The first words of welcome in our new community were, "I'll tell you where you can find a house if you help me find a new postmaster!"

We knew we were set, and in no time I found a job carrying everything from lumber to nails for builders. For the next few years, I spent most of my time in that old 6-speed International, and it was nothing like making those trips to Lebanon.

* * *

Will went to college that autumn, as he had planned, to study journalism and oration, not history; and words continued to flow from his soul as beautifully as they did in that courtroom.

Until two years ago, when Will died, we often spent summer Sundays at Hahatonka. Now, today, as we travel the highways through these hills, we always look to sight the water tower. It stands with its head in the skies and looks lonely, almost as lonely as the old post office/general store.

THE END